Dearest Son

An intimate narrative

by

Ngozi Ohoka

graceland books

Published By:
Graceland Book Publishers
2013

ISBN: 978-0956621092

All the opinions expressed in this book reflect that of the author only. This book is written for Spiritual and entertainment purpose only and is not intended to substitute for the judgement of a qualified professional.

In this work, names, characters, businesses, places, events and incidents are either the products of the author's imagination or used in a fictitious manner. Any resemblance to actual persons, living or dead, or actual events is purely coincidental.

2nd print February, 2014

Printed and bound in Ireland by PB Print Solutions,

Dedication

Dedicated to my parents, Papa and Nwa-mbu who have shared their lives these sixty-something years, brought us up and taught us the word of God.

Appreciation

My deepest appreciation goes to my husband Chikere, who has supported me throughout this work. Also to Joy Verghese, Marie Hendrick, Onyedi Victor Nwabuisi, Julie McKinley, Sandra and Felix Ogiehor, Emma Amaria Idowu and Rev. Mark Forsyth, for without them, this work will be far from complete.

References

Bill Cosby
Bishop Tudor Bismark
Dr Cindy Trim
Dr Myles Munroe
Méav Ní Mhaolchatha
Mo Abudu
Ngozi Chimaamanda Adichie
Rev. Dr. John Stephens
Rick Warren
The Holy Bible

http://boardofwisdom.com/togo/Quotes/ShowQuote?msgid=466728#.UkFrnuBsWK0

Foreward

As a Methodist Minister, I am often asked to perform many tasks for which I received no training in Bible College. Some of these tasks are difficult, while others are a joy and a privilege. Thankfully, this is in the latter category and it is an honour to be asked to introduce you to Ngozi Ohoka and this, her first published book! Over the years that I have known her, Ngozi has never failed to surprise me with her deep spirituality, her hospitality and her hidden talents. This book is the fruit of just one of those talents, and I am sure it will be the first of many.

Drawing on her treasured experiences of childhood and growing up into motherhood, Ngozi will take you on a journey of discovery, from her African heritage to her new life in Ireland. Along the way, she will share with you pearls of divine wisdom from the Scriptures, as they are applied to the rough and tumble of everyday life.

This book is written in the style of a letter from a mother to her beloved son on his wedding day, looking back over all the years that have gone before and brought them to this day. Whatever stage you have reached in life, you will be able to identify with both the author and the subject, as colourful stories tumble from the page and bring a smile to your face. Ngozi's insights reveal a deep spirituality to life, with all its ups and downs, its joys and its challenges. In an age of materialism, she writes about the things that matter most - intimate relationships, human and divine, and the daily choices that shape our destinies.

I warmly commend 'Dearest Son' to you and I am sure that it will stir your heart and bless your soul.

Rev. Mark Forsyth FSAI, BD (QUB)
Dunboyne
2013

My son, keep my teachings in your memory,
and my rules in your heart:
Proverbs 3:1

Day 1

Spring is finally here with Daffodils everywhere. Evenings take their sweet time to come and then the bright fresh morning with warm temperatures and quietness. Morning spring! I whispered to myself and just for a second wondered what inspired *Méav Ní Mhaolchatha* to sing that beautiful song, 'When Irish eyes are smiling, it's like a morning spring'. Though I didn't know the entire lyrics of the song, I was whispering and reflecting on it as I walked to the window to have a good view of that spring morning. As I was about to open the window, the birds outside started to sing. They were so happy, so chatty and so tweety that the song in my head left me and I almost joined in their conversations. The birds' songs serenaded my house and brought back life to my tired and aching body, awakening my unconscious mind. As I looked through the window, the intrinsic beauty that nature brought with it only reminded me of so many events in my life. It reminded me of my childhood, growing up, getting married, raising my children and the strangeness of getting old. I thought about my children, how sweet and beautiful they were as kids and then I thought about you; and you again. I couldn't stop thinking about you. It was so deep as though the whole of your life was a scene being played before me. I guess I would have thought about nearly everything from the beginning when you were 'nothing' to this almost unbelievable truth that you are about to be married. It was so real and so vivid that if I am an artist, I would have painted a masterpiece. But I knew I could do one thing; I could write it down.

Yes!

Brilliant idea!

Absolutely brilliant an idea - I whispered to myself. I could write you a letter and use it as a reference to point out some of the things that I knew from my own experiences that you might come across in the union that you are about to enter. For this purpose, I have reached into the deepest part of my being, a part only people like you could get into, a part of me that you already know and refer to as *mum's element* to pen down these thoughts.

You are my very first child and my first gift from God. Everyone including God pays particular attention to the first of everything. Therefore your wedding, which is the first in our family, requires so much attention. It reminds me of the first wedding in the Bible in which the Lord Jesus Christ performed his first miracle. Although I can freely make reference to this account, most importantly I have found ways to relate to it. In case you have forgotten, the story goes that there was a wedding in Cana of Galilee and lots of people were invited including Jesus and his mother Mary. In the middle of the wedding, the wine for entertainment ran out. Undoubtedly, there was trouble as a result. Perhaps no one warned the bride and groom that weddings could be such an expensive venture and that the unexpected could sometimes happen in the course of such an event. The newlyweds did not know what to do and I am particularly sure that the groom was hard hit over this uncomfortable development. Ignorantly, none of them knew that Jesus, who was by one corner, is the vine and yet they were troubled. Thank God for the timely intervention of Mary the mother of Jesus, who kindly brought their plight to the attention of Jesus, after advising them to do whatever he asked them to do.

When they came to Him, Jesus asked the men

standing there confused to pour water into the six water pots already empty; and they did. He asked them to draw from the pot and miraculously when they drew, the water became wine. This story sounded interesting to you the first time you heard it but didn't make much meaning to you until some years ago at the peak of your troubles, you used it as a point of reference to me. You would always argue, 'Mum why do you always talk against those who drink; did not Jesus himself turn water into wine?' I hope it makes some sense to you now. I have often told you that the things of the spirit always sound foolish to the person who does not have the spirit of God. The water is the Word of God. The Word is God and the six water pots standing speak of the physical man. When a man gets to a point in his life where he does and goes about things his way, he feels empty, washed out and sees no way out until someone like Mary points him to God.

The voice of God in you will invariably act

as Mary the mother of Jesus, when you are completely oblivious of His presence. The voice will urge you to apply the Word of God in this situation; pour in water into this situation that is staring you in the face. God is His word, so situations don't remain the same when God is invited or introduced into them. Note that water speaks of the Word of God. Son, if you do just that, the situation will definitely be changed. When you read the rest of the account of that miracle, it turned out that the new wine became sumptuously sweeter than the old one that ran out. So, no matter what circumstances you find yourself in the course of this journey that you are about to take, do not panic. You already have Jesus in your life and all you need is to recognise His miracle-working presence. He is our very present help in times of trouble. He does not go away or turn his back on us as some friends or family members do. He sticks with us through thick and thin. Remember, He said in His Word, 'when you go through the fire, I will be there with you'. He has promised that He 'will never leave nor forsake you'. You must know that it is not time to get worried and start complaining or getting friends involved. Get me right Son, friendship is a good thing, good friends are great gifts from the Lord and something to treasure. David and Jonathan were typical examples of what good and true friendship should be. The blood that ran in the life of their relationship was thicker than the one in brothers. Having said that, I am quite sure that David may not have involved his friend in certain decisions he took if there was no unusual covenant between them. Sometimes I wonder if David would have told Jonathan about his affair with Uriah's wife. Remember there is no friend like our true friend, Jesus. He understands every one of our intractable problems and his motives for us are good motives.

He said,

'I know the plans that I have for you, plans to do you good not evil, to bring you to an expected end'.

His motives are not like the motives of the worldly friends we have, who sometimes stab us in the back. Shakespeare, in one of his classics, 'Julius Caesar' told a gory tale of two friends; Julius Caesar and the Noble Brutus. One of them had an agenda that would eventually bring his friend to his early grave.

This poem among many others came out of this beautiful book:

Since friend to friend is so unjust,
I don't know what friend to trust.
I have trusted many to my sorrow,
Friends today, enemies tomorrow.

That was how Brutus, who was supposed to be Caesars' good friend, brutally murdered him because of his selfish ambitions. People have their secret motives, therefore you cannot entrust a thing like your marriage into the hands of your friends as they can only bring their own ignorance and ulterior motives and create more problems for you. Some of them do not have the right solutions to your problems because they don't have the right experiences. Can a blind man lead a blind man?

No is the answer, because if he does, both of them will fall into a ditch. Listening to peoples' opinions in matters of the heart may sound like those ideas out there. I am very certain that this is not what you want. What works for others may not work for you. I would strongly recommend a good counsellor if need be, rather than talking to friends about your marriage. Years ago, according to one of those stories, a man went to his friend to complain about the insoluble problem he was having with his wife. After recounting his ordeal and the trauma their kids were going through, his friend opened the Bible and showed him where it was written that wives should submit to their husbands. He went ahead to advise him to hit her if she refused to submit. Hitting her, he dutifully explained, will teach her submission. This man asked his dear friend,

'What will my children think of me when they see me hit their mother?'

His friend replied, 'Read that submission part of the Scriptures to them and don't let them ask too many questions'. There are so many friends like this friend today, who read the Bible but do not understand what they read. Remember that you are a unique person, endowed with wisdom from the Lord; you have been surrounded by people who value and respect relationships. Son, when trouble comes, you have to go to the one whose intimate acquaintance, like Shakespeare puts it, you can trust. Go to the one who has the original manual. A person who moves from one friend to another in the face of trouble seems to me like someone who is looking for a quick fix. A quick fix does not usually look at the manual and they can be described as the roadside mechanics of cars. So why go to them if you know that eventually you will need the real thing? Why involve friends who do not know the root of your troubles when you know that there is someone who understands everything and is ever willing to meet every one of your needs? There is obviously a lot that He has said to you before now and He is still willing to say more, but only if you will listen. Will you listen to Him? Always remember, I am only a shout away. I will always be your '*Mary*'; your angel who will always be in the place of intercession for you. However, you still need to play your part; obey Him, the miracle worker.

My heart jumps in excitement every time I remember that you are about to be married to the one I believe the Lord has prepared for you. The idea is thought provoking. It keeps me smiling all day and makes me walk as though I have springs under my feet. I woke up early this morning with the thought of you and I have nothing but admirations for you. I admire your courage, your faith and your firm and unwavering determination to succeed and I know certainly that God has the same admiration for you. I am nearly sure that when people look at you, the next thought in their minds will be, 'probably he was born this way' as 'everything works out well for him'. They may be right, you know; yes, you were born great just like every child of the most-high God. The difference is that you understand your strengths and you are tirelessly working on your weaknesses. You have grown into a great man with a success story. Can I jog your memory that this greatness did not just manifest over-night? No it did not. It has taken blood, sweat and tears to get you to this point. Yes Son, we have made it to this point by His grace. We have sincerely made a lot of sacrifices and so many unpopular decisions to get here. Looking back now, I can confidently say that it's really worth the journey or do you think otherwise?

When I sit down to ponder on the different events and experiences that we have been through in our lives, the joy that we came out victorious exceeds them all. Having you as a son is indeed a pleasure. Son, I am so very proud of you and I couldn't have asked for more. If I am to have another baby I would like to have another son just like you. could not think of a better way to express my joy than to write you this letter. Of course, you know that writing is something I derive pleasure doing. So can I write to you this one more time?

I have written you many letters on different occasions in your younger years but this is different now. This letter is from the deepest part of my heart and more so, I am writing you as a grown single man who is about to be married. I may not have what it takes to write you a letter as long as this in the future. For these reasons, I would like it to be well documented. I may have to type this letter and send to you by email so that you can download it to your iPhone, computer or any other electronic gadget to make it easily accessible at anytime. I am also going to print it out and put it in the post, the style I grew up with. I am sure you still have *'Postman Pat'* where you live. The content of this letter is not going to be s it is simply me reminding you ad already taught you in the past; y know, all that we experienced gether as a family and all that you heard or witnessed when it happened to other people. This letter will form a part of all you will need for your life and for this marriage journey. Or don't you know that marriage is a long journey? You are in it for the long haul, Son. This letter is therefore timely and should not be taken for granted.

Your wedding, as you may know by now is not just another reason to gather friends and family to celebrate and party. Your dad and I have decided a very long time ago, not to bring up the issue of marriage to you. Not until you are ready spiritually, emotionally and financially. This we have kept until now. Keep in mind that there are so many occasions in which you can gather people together and party; like your birthday which you always celebrate. You are not getting married because you are compelled to do so. It may sound strange but it is true that family members and parents sometimes entice children into marriages; they tell them about how their mates are all getting married and for the girls, how the biological clock is ticking away. A time like this is when you realise that some family members can be *powerful researchers*; they come up with what research has proven about the problems associated with late marriages especially if you are educated, rich and handsome like you are. They remind you about your mates who are married and have already had all their children. Only God knows how many other things such people would have told their children. Yes, they already have college degrees; they already have houses, have done this and have done that. Such pressures serve to rush you into marriage and similar milestones for which you may be unprepared only for your lack of readiness to be exposed. Eventually when a problem arises from such ill-prepared ventures, they turn around and remind you of how the separation clock is ticking. Be patient and do not rush into the future without learning the lessons from the past, be careful not to justify your hurring by the results of researches and such materials that support your intentions. Since they know what the biological clock says, could they please tell us what Abraham and Sarah's biological situations were when they could not bear a child for so long and then had it at God's appointed supernatural time? We read that when Abraham tried for a baby earlier with Hagar, based on research and human understanding, their divorce was the fastest ever recorded in the Bible. That is my view about such relationships. What do you think will happen Son, when a teacher promotes a child who has not done well in class; or an employer who hires an applicant without enough experience or training? You know better than I do, so give me the answer. Time is of essence here; timing has to do with God's will and our preparedness. Have you ever seen that quote; *'in His time, He makes all things beautiful'*. When it is His time, we won't see the ugly, rather the beautiful; we won't see the crooked but the straight; we won't see weaknesses, we will see strength; we won't see poverty but abundance; we won't see the imperfect but the perfect. All the missing pieces of the puzzles are brought together when it is His appointed time and everything will be all so good. Put in another way, can one set a goal for another? Personally I don't think it is right to do so. I was reading through some quotes the other day and I saw this beautiful writing of a mother's reflection, which reads:

> *I gave you life, but cannot live it for you.*
>
> *I can teach you things, but I cannot make you learn.*
>
> *I can give you directions, but I cannot be there to lead you.*
>
> *I can allow you freedom, but I cannot account for it.*
>
> *I can take you to church, but I cannot make you believe.*
>
> *I can teach you right from wrong, but I cannot always decide for you.*

I can buy you beautiful clothes, but I cannot make you beautiful inside.

I can offer you advice, but I cannot accept it for you.

I can give you love, but I cannot force it upon you.

I can teach you to share, but I cannot make you unselfish.

I can teach you respect, but I cannot force you to show honour.

I can advise you about friends, but cannot choose them for you.

I can advise you about sex, but I cannot keep you pure.

I can tell you the facts of life, but I can't build your reputation.

I can tell you about drink, but I can't say "no" for you.

I can warn you about drugs, but I can't prevent you from using them.

I can tell you about lofty goals, but I can't achieve them for you.

I can teach you about kindness, but I can't force you to be gracious.
I can warn you about sins, but I cannot make you moral.
I can love you as a child, but I cannot place you in God's family.
I can pray for you, but I cannot make you walk with God.
I can teach you about Jesus, but I cannot make Jesus your Lord.
I can tell you how to live, but I cannot give you eternal life.
I can love you with unconditional love all of my life...and I will!

Author - unknown

Because I can, I will by His grace continue to love you unconditionally. We have been patient with you, allowing you to do things at your pace but only guided you to do things when you are ready. Jesus, who is our spiritual husband, is still waiting for us to be ready. That's why He still has not come for us; He is waiting for a bride without spot or wrinkles so that when He comes, we will be like Him; talk like Him and have the same expression as His. The same is true in marriage. I hope you know by now that it is a union that God has made to bring out one expression from two people. This is the reason the devil is not happy with marriages. He hates to see that single expression. He hates a peaceful and united front; he always pretends to be around the corner picking on you, attacking from all sides and never happy for you to fulfil the will of God for your life. He is forever fighting and tempting you, while God on the other hand is watching and cheering you on because he has already prepared you. Yes, He sits on the throne and cheers you on because He has fought the battle and won the victory for you, even though it may not always be apparent, otherwise He wouldn't have allowed the devil to come near Job. Sometimes He allows you to practice what you have learnt from His Word as He has already equipped you with the whole armour of God. So, as the bad man tempts to see you fail, God watches to see you overcome. So for God, it is a test, one you have to pass. Remember where the Bible admonished us to *'fight the good fight of faith'*. So here now, you are going to apply every tactic you have learnt from Master J in the Taekwondo class. You will use every technique he had ever taught you; all the muscles you have built over time must come to work now. Are you surprised that I still remember your Taekwondo class and teacher? How can I possibly forget when I sat there every Tuesday evening listening to your teacher's voice, with its refreshing candour? I sat there cheering you as God cheers us when we fight our spiritual battles. I vividly remember the day you were to fight in a competition. I had received a text message from Master J, asking if you would like a fight. You jumped at that invitation and we were looking forward to it for three whole weeks. I had paid for that fight and you had practiced a little in preparation. When the big day came, we all went to the centre with you and we realised you were paired with a red belt, a level higher than yours. The moment you saw him, butterflies started flying in your stomach, you looked me in the eye and said,

'Mum I don't think I want to fight anymore'. You were in a lower belt category at the time and I was confused as well. I didn't know what to do. I have heard about people giving pep talk before a competition but I have never given any. I quickly put on a happy bold face and was ready to give my very first pep talk. I urged you to go and fight; as you took a step, you looked back but I sat there nodding in response to our earlier conversation. Just as the fight was about to begin I ran up to you and reminded you of the story of David and Goliath, how David fought even in the face of a rather difficult situation. You smiled and went against him just like David with only five stones went against Goliath with his array of military might. Son, I could not believe that you knocked him down more than three times before the fight ended in your favour. You were so proud of yourself and so was I. Yes, you are going to use that same zeal but remember you must follow the rules or else you will be defeated. Suffice it to say that the set of rules is the Word of God and every piece of good advice your dad and I ever gave you. You loved the fight between David and Goliath as a child and like you know, Goliath represents every bad thing you can think of. He talks down on the people of God and bullies them just like the enemy the devil would like to bully your marriage. One day, David who is anointed of God fought and defeated him and won the battle. You have the Word of God in you, the same anointing David had, so you are fully equipped to stand against the devil to fight and defeat him. It's not that God couldn't have fought Goliath on behalf of David; no, He could have done that but there are some things that God would like you to do yourself. Take for instance all the years you were growing up, I never came out to defend you when bad boys bullied you. I remember when some silly boys were bullying you when you were a little boy, you always ran back to complain. I did not go up to any of them to try to stop them, instead all I did was to equip you by telling you how to stand up for yourself and put them to shame; you did those things and they worked out. The only fight I ever came out to fight for you, if you could remember, was the day a man drove into our estate while you were playing in the open field and ran over your new BMX bike. If you can recollect, all those boys you were playing with cried out and ran to our house and of course you cried with them. As soon as I came out and saw a man loading furniture into his van without pity or any sense of remorse over the cries of all the kids, I took him on. I knew immediately that it was a fight I had to fight for my son and his friends. To worsen the situation, the man was looking at me as if to say 'what can you do' and I felt challenged. He was indirectly asking me what can you do now that your son and his friends have called you. I had no other option but to call the police. The summary of it all was that the police forced him to repair the bike. It is worthy of note that when something higher than us comes to us, it challenges God. He does not keep quiet but steps up to it. When He actually feels challenged like I felt, He quickly gets up from His throne of mercy to fight for us, to deliver us from the forces that are mightier than us. Other than that, you have to take your place in battle and fight the good fight of faith. So go in the name of Jesus and in the power of His might. However, you may need to fight more than just one battle but always remember that the rule is the same. The enemy is the same, but as long as you remain in God's Camp, your victory is always assured.

Have you ever wondered why individuals, groups, institutions and nations fight? Some of the numerous reasons would include protecting their interests, insatiable longings, trying hard to take what does not belong to them or maybe fighting to stop what they think would hurt them. Remember the Nigerian-Biafran war and the endless lists of Nations fighting against one another. Just as the devil is fuelling these wars among nations, he is also fighting against families. In truth, the World will be a better place when family members are at peace with each other. This explains why the devil constantly attacks relationships and families. Therefore you have a task to protect this good thing God has given you and a duty to ward off the enemy. You really have to be on the offensive. Remember, you are not to be ignorant of the devices of the enemy for he comes to steal, to kill and to destroy and because he is a coward, he always disguises himself. Think about it, why would a man fight his wife over the least of things; or why do couples that are madly in love with each other at the beginning find themselves in the court of Law? Could things not be discussed over the breakfast table or even in the usual way? All of a sudden, they cannot bear the sight of each other as they become worst enemies.

Sometimes when children are involved, they do not care about the emotional needs of these children whom they once loved and cherished. Could you believe it if I told you Son, that the causes of these rifts and crisis in the home are normally very insignificant issues? They build a mountain out of a molehill when things are not put into proper perspective; they are easily blown out of proportion. The devil is an expert in exaggerating issues but most times he does not start the trouble; people do and then the devil amplifies it. Once you create a loophole, you give him room to begin to act. You are inviting him to come in and do what he derives joy in doing; he makes sure that a huge monster is made out of nothing. When one sits down to reflect on the events that preceded the ugly development, one will find out that there was really nothing serious. A statement as little as *I am sorry* would have fixed a huge problem. So will you learn to nip every ugly developing issue in the bud? Another way you can do this is to allow God to deal with you first; allow Him to see your dark side and submit to His cleansing. Most times we cover our dark side but it will take a relationship that is as new as yours for some minor issues in our lives to be revealed. Then you hear someone exclaim *if I knew him to be this bad, I sure would not have married him or I would have gone for the other person.* Open up to God now; open up to her as well because you both still have a choice. A broken engagement they say is better than a broken marriage. Remember, it may only hurt for a short while. You have always had very good negotiating skills; your dad and I had always thought you would make a good lawyer because of the way you dialogued with us in the past. Will you bring out that nature and put it to good use in this relationship? Make sure you do not impose your ideas on her, as I am sure she will like to be heard. If one person wins, the relationship suffers. As much as it is possible, do not to let any matter escalate, it may not be easy to handle afterwards.

Hmmm! I have a feeling that this letter is going to be a very long one and I am simply asking God to give me the grace to write it all. As I write, I keep remembering all that we have discussed in the past; all that I have taught you and all that you have learnt the from influential people in your life. I also pray that God will open your eyes of understanding as you read through. I also know that I will get a reply from you someday. Son, please do not be too mindful when replying this letter, you can ask questions to clarify issues that have been raised in this letter which you may not understand or which might be a bit confusing. The best person to ask for clarifications most times is the person who raised an issue. Because I have written this letter, ask me for clarifications if you are in doubt; it has to be so because I understand the reasons for writing this letter. This is same with the Word of God, which is also His letter to us. It could be overwhelming to someone who does not understand the ways of the Lord. Perhaps that is the reason why some people run here and there to get interpretations; forgetting that this book or letter has an author and the best person to interpret it or produce the reason behind the writing is the person who wrote the book.

On my own path, I will try not to use high sounding-words; I will keep it very simple. Remember that I am still your beloved mum. If I confuse you, then the whole aim is defeated. However I am convinced that your eyes of understanding will be enlightened.

I guess that I have lost count of time writing this letter but must take a rest now to attend to other issues here. One of dad's friends is coming over for dinner with his wife and I need to get ready for them.

I get very excited every time I remember that your wedding is only a few months away. I still can't believe that the baby I had a couple of years back has grown as big as to be getting married very soon. It seems just like yesterday as time they say, really flies. I went into your room the other day and was looking through the memories we shared. That phrase jumped out of my mouth: *"Mum, are we in September yet"*. As long as I live I will never forget that month of

September together with the months, weeks and days preceding it. September has always been the beginning of a new academic year and the September of the year you started school was a very special September for all of us. I am quite sure it was the one September that ever meant so much to you. It was the September when you were to go into *big school*. As soon as you knew that, it got stuck in your mind. You so desperately wanted September to come, that every day you would wake up and ask me if it was September yet. You could not walk pass the uniform section in a Shopping Mall without talking about your uniform for September. You wanted every fancy looking cartoon character bag for a school bag in September. I remember one day in July of that year, I could not hear any sound of you and I got so scared. I looked for you everywhere in the house, only to find you at one corner of your closet cleaning and polishing all your shoes with an old shirt and Vaseline oil. When I asked you what you were doing, you said: *getting my shoes ready for September* like dad would get his shoes ready if he was to go to somewhere important. *Mum, just getting my shoes ready for September like you told me*. Can I say that you acted just like Jesus who could not wait for His time to come for him to do the work of his Father. He was ready for His mission long before he came down to the earth. When he finally came, at one time after a feast in Jerusalem, he stayed back. He did not go home with his parents. His parents did not know where He was and were worried as they looked for him everywhere. When they eventually found him in the temple, he told them that he wanted to do the work of his Father. He knew that it was not yet time and his parents knew that as well and that was why they were troubled. However, when the time was ripe, no one looked for him anymore.

In your case, you did not know that it was not time yet. You could not wait at all, you wanted to leave *baby school* as you called it then and go to a proper school but I needed you to wait and to grow in strength and wisdom; to be able to take in information from your teacher and be able to stand up to the boys and girls who like to bully others. You needed to develope the ability to withstand the demands that *big school* would bring. Unfortunately, in the year you were to join the big school, the school policy changed. New students were to be four years by the first of May preceding the September and that meant you were going to stay for another year as you were to be four by the end of that May. That news made you cry, you lamented on how the principal has ruined your whole life and how it was not fair but nevertheless, you waited. You never stopped asking me whether the principal did that to your dad and I when we were about to start big school. My reply Son, was that the principal meant it for good; I also told you that we had a different principal and so everything was different. Policies can be different from one school to another and from one country to another. During my days Son, you had to be able to touch your left ear with your right fingers across your head. If you fell short of doing that by an inch, you knew that you were not ready to start primary school. It was very different as their concern then was physical development only. These days, a childs maturity is judged by the child's level of intellectual development and ability to recognise and handle their emotions. They may have seen that you were really not ready emotionally. I am sure that if it was during my time, your palm would have conveniently covered your left ear because you were big for your age. They were not looking at your height but they were concerned about your emotions. I suppose no teacher would like to teach a child who tears up all the time.

Thankfully, we still had the kindergarten which you called baby school and the Sunday school. To tell you the truth, Sunday school is the best school any child can attend. It is the foundation for a child's learning. You loved Sunday school and you looked forward to Sundays, especially the treat you got after Church from your Sunday school teacher. You loved the Bible stories, especially coming up to Christmas when there would be the nativity play that told about the birth of Jesus Christ. Your role would always be one of the shepherds and we already knew that we would be converting the tea towel and your housecoat into a shepherd's outfit. You loved it a lot and you looked forward to it. Most of all, you loved the songs especially:

Jesus loves me this I know,
For the Bible tells me so,
Little ones to him belong
They are weak but he is strong
Chorus:
Yes, Jesus loves me
Yes, Jesus loves me
Yes, Jesus loves me
The Bible tells me so.

You also used the tune to sing many other songs. It was quite funny the way you sang those songs. Most times you screamed with all the veins and arteries shooting out from your neck as though if you didn't, we would not hear you. It used to be very funny but I knew that the Lord was enjoying the songs and praises; after all it was all for Him and Him alone. You wanted me to see the actions that go with each song and I had to leave whatever I was doing to pay full attention and clap when asked to do so and then give you a big hug at the end. You loved singing, talking and reading aloud to yourself. The truth was that most of your books and Bible stories came with large prints and large photographs and because you had memorised most of the stories, you would flip through them and retell the stories. Sometimes the stories you told was not sequential with the pages of the book and at other times the book was placed upside down! However, you continued to read and you derived lots of pleasure doing that. So Sunday school and baby school kept you going until the next

September. We all saw the result of your waiting as your principal and teacher acknowledged that you were very mature in everything. You were quite capable and highly competent in all your academic work. You knew the answers to nearly all the questions the teacher asked in class and you would come home bragging about it. I would always reply by asking *can you see the reason why I gave you those fruit and vegetables you didn't like?* I did that anyway because I knew that they were good for you and they actually helped to develop your brain and your muscles. No wonder God wants us to produce the fruit of the spirit, which is love, joy, peace, long-suffering, kindness, goodness, faithfulness, gentleness and self-control. When we have them as children of God, we will be able to face any situation in our lives; we will take higher responsibilities in our Christian living, develop spiritual muscles and mature properly.

We were on holidays that summer before the

school year began and you kept asking if it was September yet. One morning you came to dad and asked the same question and when he told you *not yet*, you said that your worry was that we may be here enjoying the summer and would not realise when September would come and go. You had already memorised the name of your teacher from the letter that was sent months before and you were so curious, you wanted to know who your friends would be, what you would see, and what your classroom would look like. You couldn't stop asking questions, just as I could not stop answering, no matter how tired I was. I remember the lunch bag you chose; you made me buy a very big one so you could go to school with a large lunch just in case any child forgot theirs at home. I told you it was alright to share but that you must first get permission from the teacher in case a certain child is not allowed to eat anything in your lunch box for any reason. On hearing this, you looked at me with doubtful expression and asked:

Why mum?

I said to you:

For some religious or health reasons.

I knew you did not get that when you replied back and said to me:

But in baby school we ate everything together and no one got sick.

Finally, it was September but we still had to endure this agony until Monday the 18th. The night before your first day at school was probably the longest night of your life and it was not easy for your dad and I either. We had ironed your uniforms and you made sure that we left them for you on your room door handle; your school tie was just by your pillow; you did not want to look for your tie or socks in the morning as dad would sometimes do. You had already packed your lunch box and kept it in the refrigerator. You came twenty times or so, waking us up and asking:

Mum, dad, *is it morning yet? Can I go and dress*

up for school now?

We understood that it was not just another way of seeking attention, which you were used to. Once you woke up early as a child, everyone in the house had to wake up. However that morning, we understood that enthusiasm, excitement, anxiety and curiosity and did not confuse it with any abnormality. We were equally excited that our little boy was ready for school. Normally in many families, that day approaches with mixed feelings of anticipation and apprehension for both parents and children. This was our situation that morning. I wondered what activities would occupy you for the two or three hours you were required to stay for the first week. We were concerned about you, although confident that you would be all right as you were already prepared and the time was ripe too. Your school was located about fifteen minutes away from our house and we had been there several times to meet with your teachers and other pupils enrolling in the school that year at the *Open Day*.

At long last, we were ready to go to school. Before we could get there that morning, you had asked me five times whether we had gotten there yet. From the back seat of the car where you were seated, all I could hear was:

Mum, are we there yet, when are we getting there?

My response was *not yet*. To worsen the situation, that was a busy Monday morning and traffic was a bit heavy with lots of commuters - people going to work and others doing the school run as well. I knew it was going to be so that morning, so I decided we would leave a little early to help the situation. In the end, we were there just in time to join the line before the school bell rang. Thanks to the lollipop lady who was effortlessly directing traffic with one hand while holding her lollipop stick on the other. To see her stand in the middle of the road and ably commanding traffic that morning really amazed you. You were completely in awe and could not resist the urge to ask:

Mum, does the lollipop lady stay here all day? Is

that her job?

'No, she's only here to help us get by safely and she will return to her house until the afternoon when school is over.'

To see you line up that morning with the other children only confirmed to me that you were such an independent child. Your uniform of black trousers, white shirt, Gray jumper and tie fitted you perfectly. You looked like a newly conscripted baby military personnel. You wore your schoolbag on your back desperately trying to show off the power-rangers character printed on it. Meanwhile it had nothing close to books or writing materials in it, rather it contained a power-rangers lunch box that had sandwiches, a drink and a piece of apple that I was very sure would come back home with you untouched. I was also not sure you were going to eat the sandwiches because you were only meant to spend three hours a day for the first week. Moreover, I had talked you into eating your breakfast, telling you that you will be stronger and more intelligent in class if you eat your cereal in the morning before going to school. I also showed you a research done by the producers of Kellogg's products that showed that children who eat their breakfast are found to be more intelligent than those who did not. The manufacturers' strategy was especially targeted at children, with their bright packaging on the cereal packs that sometimes came with tiny gifts and things to win. They also placed them as adverts on the children's television programmes every 15 minutes to entice them. I am one person that never believed wholly what manufacturers write about their products to impress consumers. However, when it is something that will help us in our family relationships, I don't mind using them. I am sure you will never forget *Green Giant*. They advertised sweet corn and you wanted so much to grow your muscles but you would never go near your fruit and vegetables. I kept talking to you about *Green Giant* and made sure you notice their advert as many times as they flashed it and it really worked wonders for us.

As soon as the school bell rang, you flew into your classroom and made straight for the coat hangers. We were advised to write your name on every one of your belongings and your name was already pasted on the rack where you would hang your coat for the term. You sat with your arms stretched out across the blue table and sitting opposite was a child who could not even look away from her parents for one second. This child's parents were even worse than the child as her mother was sobbing uncontrollably. I felt like going to ask the teacher whether you guys were still going to do three hours or a whole day and night. Those parents made me feel as though you were all dropped in a boarding house in the middle of nowhere. Anyway, I felt compassion for them and tried to empathise with them. The other two seats in your table were empty at this stage while you were already settled; the empty seats probably belonged to those kids whose mums were still trying to persuade to stay while you did not seem to notice that we were standing there. Indeed you were ready for that level in your life. As we waved for you to look up for a first day photograph, you were busy looking at yourself, looking at your uniform from top to bottom, dusting off some lint or thread you had seen on your trousers in the bright classroom light. We captured that moment in pictures and have kept it for you so that in years to come, you would treasure the memory or even show them to your own children. I stood there wondering what was going on in your mind as your eyes were moving up and down. Were you thinking that your teachers were coming for an inspection or did you have any expectations that you did not discuss with us? We could not even take a proper photograph of you or with you, although we managed to get something as we also came with a video camera. As you felt cool and cared less about our presence, some mums were asked to stay a little longer just to ensure that their children settled in properly. You were perfect and to be truthful with you, your teacher did not even look at us twice as she busied herself with more difficult cases. Everyone noticed your independence and keenness to be in school. You made me such a proud mum. I remember a mother who walked up to ask me some general questions about us; where we live, how long it took us to get to school and if she could pick you up to play with her son sometimes. I actually thought that she was being friendly but little did I know that she wanted you to be friends with her son, so that you could affect him with your courage. Finally, she succeeded and sometimes would come to our house early to pick you up to ginger her own son to go to school. You cannot believe it Son, that when her son settled down eventually, I would see her at the school gate, wave at her and say hello to her but she would pretend not to know me anymore.

You loved school right from the very beginning and it is a big credit to you. Sincerely speaking, I thought that after one week, you were going to quit and say, ‘I have seen it all’, given the level of excitement at which you started but you did not. In fact, like in *Timothy goes to school*, that children’s programme you loved to watch on television as a child, every single day in school became an adventure. Like Timothy, you believed that in every brand new day anything could happen when Timothy goes to school. You were full of news, full of stories of who played with who, who ate with who at the table, the children you recognised from your baby school, the stars and rewards the teacher gave you. On the first day you came back with a star and told us that your table, which was blue, would likely get a star every day for the rest of the week. You said you were nearly certain you would get it because you all did everything the teacher told you to do. I asked you:

Things like what?

You said: ‘like placing a finger on the lips, not talking when the teacher was talking, and raising your hand if you wanted to say something and then waiting to be called'.

I was happy that they were already introducing social skills and teamwork to you at that stage. Team play was what you did when your table worked together to win that star. Then you added, 'I think school is not as difficult as people say it is because all the things we did in baby school are still the things we're doing in the big school.'

Things like what? I asked you.

'My teacher separated four balls into two today and asked us to add them together. Can you do that mum?'

'No', I answered.

'Then I can teach you. It means that two balls and another two balls would make four balls'. Is there any other way to get the answer? No mum, the only way is the way our teacher said we should do it. 'You're really a genius', I told you. You just wanted to be congratulated all the way.

Little did you know that the learning in baby school would continue in Junior Infant School.

That's what they call *look back*.

Then you asked:
'Mum, when are we going to start learning to become Doctors and Engineers like Uncle Uche, and Auntie Amaka?'

You were all out for it and as far as you were concerned, there were no limitations. You wanted to reach out for the stars immediately and wondered why you were kept for so long in the baby school. You came back with new stories and news everyday; news of how the Principal made an announcement on the *PA Systems* and how everyone got to hear it from their classrooms. You memorised what the Principal said and how she said it. You told me about your new friends. One of them, you said, could not clean the snot coming out from his nose; he was busy licking the snot and rubbing it with the back of his palm. You talked about the senior buddies that were allocated to you from the senior classes. You told me that your teacher came to school with a big teddy bear, which she gave to pupils in turn and the teddy had to come back to school with the person the next day. The teddy would go round to every child's home, you told me. Within me, I knew that your teacher was wise, because you couldn't refuse to go to school the next day, knowing that you needed to return the big teddy for another child to take home. You looked forward to when it will be your turn to host the big teddy. You told me that you were going to give the teddy a name and sleep with him the night he visits. You talked about your new friends every day, how you met them and how you were going to help them if they ever got into trouble or needed your help.

'Mum, I think one of my friends will need my help'. 'What sort of help?' I asked.

'Don't bother mum, my teacher said we should not talk about it anymore, therefore it's a secret.' Just hearing that word secret, I knew that I needed to have a conversation with you. I quickly washed off the soap on my hands, dried it up with the tea towel that hung on my neck and came over to you. I gently spoke to you that family members do not keep secrets from one another and that whatever happens in school must be freely discussed at home with mum or dad. So as I heard that word *secret*, I said no, I must stop this secrecy now. I sat you on my lap and gently urged you to tell me why your friend was in trouble, what happened to him and why it was a secret.

'Please mum, don't talk to anyone about it because our teacher would not be happy that we discussed it with anyone.' You pleaded.

'I am not just anyone Son, I am your mum'

I urged you on and on to tell me and promised that I would keep it a secret, though not sure how far I could go with keeping some sort of secret that could be risky. You looked around and made me to close the kitchen door and made sure no one else was listening and you said:

'Do you remember the boy that I told you about the other day, the boy who could not speak English?'

Yes I do, I remember him, what about him?'

'He had an accident today.' You whispered into my ear. Then I responded 'Oh! So sorry, poor him.

'You see mum, that is why I told you that I will be helping some of them when they are in trouble'.
'So how will you help this friend?' I asked.
'I am going to help him to speak. Before this accident, I saw him get up; he went to the teacher and said something. But I don't think that the teacher heard him very well. I am going to be his friend and teach him how to say things so that other people can understand him.

You came back another day and proudly told me how you were sent on a message to another class, that all the boys and girls in that class said hello to you at the same time and their class teacher gave you a treat. I was amazed at your confidence. You went on and on and you were always full of news whenever I came to collect you. You were always happy and *chatty* with your friends. From the gate I was always hearing things like:
'Bye Luke, bye Sally, bye Obi, see you later Alligator, in a while Crocodile, *Slán*.'
'What does *Slán* mean?' I asked you one afternoon.

'Mum, that is the Irish word for goodbye, we were taught that on the first day.'

'I am impressed you were taught that already, I replied.

'Yes we were.'

'When you say *Slán* to someone, their reply should be *Slán* too. Does it sound cool mum?'

'Yes it does sound cool, especially when you say it. Can I say that to you when I drop you off in the morning?'

'Well, I don't think mums are allowed to use that word.

Just tell me bye and see you later.'

'Okay I will do just as you say.'

'That reminds me mum, there are some French and German children in my class, would you know how they say their goodbyes?'

'Yes I do. The French say *au revoir* and the Germans say *auf wiedersehen.*'

'Sounds very cool too'. Can I learn it and say that to them as well?'

'Sure you can. You can learn any good thing you

want to learn and be whatever you want to be.'

'Mum?'

'Yes?'

'Why did God create so many languages?'

'Variety Son, God loves variety and maybe that was the reason why He created people with different colours and shapes. Variety they say, is the spice of life.' I knew you were having some real fun. These are some of the memories going on in my mind as I look through things that remind me that you once lived here, in this room.

Your school books are still the very way you made me to pack them before you left, the textbooks separately packed from the workbooks. I was reading through your 3rd class report and I saw your teacher's comments and a tear dropped down my cheek. Her words were exactly who you are; very hardworking, excellent in your writing, dedicated, very competitive and honest. Dear Son, to tell you the truth, that was who you really were, until you became a teenager and realised that you are grown up and thought that the world would end the next day. But thank God that you came to your senses soon enough. I hope you don't change anymore as men they say, change in the face of difficult situations and challenges. But guess what? Real men are not moved by difficulties. I am convinced that you are well trained. Your dad and I can give God and ourselves that credit; at least we tried our best. 'Train up a child in the way he should go and when he is old, he will not depart from it.' The Bible told us that and we trained you according to the Word of God, as we taught you good morals and left inside of you the basic human values. I am and will be praying for you and surely you will overcome, because you have been equipped with every good and perfect gift from God.

Back to the books in your room, what do you want me to do with them? Should I give them away to charity or hold on to them till you visit? You know you two are always welcome. Your favourite aeroplane posters are still on the wall. Growing up, you changed your mind every year on what you would like to be when you grew up. First, you were asked in the class about what you wanted to be when you grew up and your answer was that you want to be a teenager. In the year of the aeroplane posters, we came back from a holiday and had loved the aircraft we travelled in. You were so impressed that you said to me:

'Mum, I think I want to be a pilot when I grow up.'

'Why, I asked?'

'So that I could get all those nice treats from the cabin crew every day.'

So for that whole season, you wanted to be a pilot.

Just under the computer table in your room, I saw that little box in which you put some of your most cherished treasures. I found two of your loose teeth and an envelope containing some class photos. I think those photos were junior and senior infant classes. I could not stop laughing, just looking at those cheerful smiles with half of the teeth gone in almost all the mouths. Some of them have their molars already poking their way through. Yours was so pronounced Son and I still can't forget how the tip of your tongue would subconsciously stick out through the wide gap between your teeth. To worsen the situation, you wanted the whole world to know that your tooth had fallen out. You wanted your aunts and uncles to know and you made sure that was part of my telephone conversations to every relative I spoke with. You wanted the conversations to be about the tooth and the golden coin from the tooth fairy; how your mum did not believe in the tooth fairy, but had to give you some coins from her pocket instead.

'Were all those boys and girls I saw in the photograph like that?' I wondered.

'Were their mothers responding to their demanding and inquisitive behaviours like me?'

'Did they all find coins under their pillows from the supposed tooth fairy whenever they lost a tooth?'

I wondered what their impressions now are about the lies, as I am sure they have all eventually discovered that they were being lied to. I wondered sometimes where the boys and girls are and what has become of them; whether they all have copies of these photographs and what goes through their minds when they look at them. Life is really in stages Son, some of them will exclaim like me. I will leave them here if you want, be rest assured you will find them the way you left them. Should you be wondering, a few of your other possessions have been carefully packed away in the attic and they will be there as long as you want me to keep them.

I saw your favourite bed cover, the one with the logo of the football club you supported and I am very sure you will still want it. It is one of the things I have packed away and believe it or not, it is still as good as new, far better than what they have in the shops these days. I remember the day I bought that for you, it was on your seventh birthday and your dad thought that I was crazy for spending that much money on an item like that. But it was one of the ways of your old mum, for which you would remember me for and one of my favourite quotes was: '*you buy cheap, you buy twice*'. You cannot cut corners. People often make poor choices and then they have to go back and re-do things. If the Lord wanted Moses and the children of Israel to cut corners, he would have done that but he didn't, for the fear that if they found things too easy, they might not be able to stand in the face of difficult situations. He made them to go the long but right route. If you think about it, when you decided to buy a house, you saw houses that were cheap and apparently not very well located. When your friends encouraged you to buy that particular house because they loved it there, you vehemently refused. Could it be that you learned that basic life-principle from your mum? Have it on your mind that there is a difference between poor choice and cheap choice. I am only saying that you were wise. You could afford to buy from either location but you made the right choice. You have also made the right choice to find a girl and settle down with her as your wife. I know that some of your friends go from one girl to another, without considering the consequences. Some of them think that it does not really matter; others think that it is the right process towards getting the right girl. Your decision to marry a girl who honours and fears the Lord is the best you had ever made; it's a step towards the right direction. Whoso *findeth* a wife, *findeth* a good thing and *obtaineth* favour from the Lord. You may never have to look for another wife. Note, I say 'may' here, because a part of her is still being transformed just like you. Together you will both transform and influence yourselves and your generation. There are so many things you may not know about her; remember human beings have a natural tendency to fight first, then put their best foot forward in life. Everyone has a subconscious dark side, everyone has a dirty side that they don't want someone else to see and it's only God that sees and knows these sides of us. That is why the Psalmist says:

'Search me oh Lord, and know my heart,
Try me oh Lord, and know my heart I pray,
See if there is some wicked way in me,
Cleanse me from every sin and set me free'

So Son, it is in a relationship that you get a thorough revelation and knowledge of a person, and you will be amazed to know that you also have hidden issues worth knowing about. No wonder the Bible says that the only perfect one is God. My prayer is that when you get this full revelation, the enabling power of God will keep you two and help you two to work it out together. That was exactly what happened with that bed sheet and we never had to buy another.

Lately I have been looking at wedding magazines and websites, just to get myself familiarised with what happens on these occasions these days. I wonder what you two have been planning or considering? I don't want to sound or look uninformed about this occasion. You know it's been ages since your dad and I got married and as expected, a good number of things have drastically changed. It was during the course of my investigation that I realised that there are even wedding events and shows planned so that intending couples and their families can attend to help them with their big day's decisions. Sometimes there are competitions set up by these agencies to be won by the best couples. Some go as far as collaborating with television stations for such promotions to be aired or advertised. A few days ago, we went to one of such fairs and saw a group of young couples queuing up with numbers pinned ceremoniously to their clothes. When I asked them what was going on, I was rightly informed that they had entered the competition for their weddings to be sponsored and that the result of the competition would be released that day. The concept and the delightful ambiance of the environment astounded me. I asked what they had to do to win the competition and was told that they were to answer some simple questions like how they met and how they knew that they had made the right decisions. Son, I imagined you there, telling them that you prayed about yours and that the spirit of God convinced you that she is the one. I am sure that if that happened, it will be given a ridiculous caption in the news because most people operating at that level are clueless about the things of God. But that could also be an opportunity to tell people about God.

Most couples now subtly tell you what they want for their wedding presents, some of them go as far as setting up a wedding register with a department store, where friends and relatives can buy presents without fear of duplicity. Couples may decide to marry anywhere ranging from boats to gardens and to Churches. I also noticed that outfits have changed so much from the traditional long white gown and suit. Some brides now wear pink or red if they wish and they can even have a change of clothes for the reception. There has also been the introduction of dress codes - friends could be asked to wear colours to match the hall decorations or the bride bouquet, black tie or cocktail dresses. In some traditions, the parents of the bride and groom wear clothes that are uniform. I must say that it is a different world that I am living in now and it's quite unbelievable how things have changed. Then on the wedding day, other side attractions are provided like the magician, sweet booth, fireworks and whatever else you can imagine. Sometimes, I don't even know where I live anymore. Some people say that it is technology and I am forced to believe this because all these are marriages of different cultures that are now transmitted through the media. The changes are quite rapid and somewhat troubling. Although everything changes, even human beings, I am afraid it sometimes happens rather too quickly. Son, these days, depending on the kind of wedding you are hoping to have, there are the wedding planners but just for the records, be careful of whom you get involved with. If you are eventually going to get a planner, which I know you will, there are so many of them out there, some of them are recognised while others are not even registered. These un-registered ones have their adverts everywhere and are after money to enrich themselves, leaving you stranded on your wedding day. But that will not happen to you because you are a very careful person, cautious and meticulous in your decisions and choices. Don't take things for granted here. Remember, the arm of flesh shall fail you; only depend on God's wisdom and ability. I am not saying that bad things do not happen to good and careful people; no, not at all. All that I am saying is that you have to be wise. Note, the Bible says that only simpletons believe everything they are told! The prudent carefully consider their steps. Depend on God's wisdom and trust that God will direct and perfect that which concerns you. If they don't work out, you can turn to God and have good reasons to have a decent dialogue with him. Remember that song we like to sing nearly every night during prayer time – 'What a friend we have in Jesus'?

Here are the full lyrics of that song by Joseph M. Scriven, written in 1855:

1 What a friend we have in Jesus,
All our sins and griefs to bear!
What a privilege to carry
Everything to God in prayer!
O what peace we often forfeit,
O what needless pain we bear,
All because we do not carry
Everything to God in prayer!

2. Have we trials and temptations?
Is there trouble anywhere?
We should never be discouraged;
Take it to the Lord in prayer.
Can we find a friend so faithful?
Who will all our sorrows share?
Jesus knows our every weakness;
Take it to the Lord in prayer.

3. *Are we weak and heavy laden?*
Cumbered with a load of care?
Precious Saviour, still our refuge;
Take it to the Lord in prayer.
Do thy friends despise, forsake thee?
Take it to the Lord in prayer!
In his arms he'll take and shield thee;
Thou wilt find a solace there.

You could not ask for a better friend at this stage of your life. You have to always talk to and confide in Him before you take any decision, like I taught you. 'Trust in the Lord with all your heart and lean not on your own understanding; in all your ways acknowledge him, and he will direct your path' Wisdom belongs to Him, that's the reason why you need Him. You must trust him because He will never let you down or lead you the wrong way. Son, no matter how you plan, no matter what professionals you are involved with, if you don't involve God, the planning will not work out. As for anything you commit into His hands, you can be quite sure that He will keep it safe and secure, even the planning of your wedding.

So, concerning the planners, the wedding planners these days will delve into so many things ranging from finding you a perfect location to getting your bride's dress. But remember, a wedding is a very personal thing and at the end of the day, it is only you and your bride who will make decisions concerning the type of the wedding you would like to have. Your wedding can be a reflection of who you are. I may be wrong here, so please correct me if I am. Handing away all the planning may mean handing out your identity and your entire person to someone else. Having known you for a long time, you don't want to do that. I know who you are Son, your likes and dislikes, although your wife-to-be will find out more. One of the things you don't like is a big crowd. Maybe you have changed. You have always not liked crowds or are things different now? In those days when I hosted womens' social meetings and they

spoke at the top of their voices, you would draw me to one corner and ask me,
'Mum, when is your meeting with this bunch of women coming to an end?
Is it not our dinner time yet?
Are they having dinner with us?
Do they have children?
Are their children our ages?
Who will make dinner for their children?'
You did that a number of times until one day I had to call you aside to find out why you always asked all those questions as often as people come to the house. It was then that you informed me that their number is a bit high and they don't ever take turns to talk and most times they don't listen to one another. According to you, all they did talk about was fashion and the new clothes coming out in the shops. Unfortunately Son, you are going to draw people together at this special event. They will come as witnesses to testify that your marriage did happen. Your relationship with your fiancee is no longer going to be a secret one

after that day. So they will come to witness your union and to support you. Some of them may be married and so their presence on that day will be to encourage and support you to go on because they have been through it themselves. Remember, as Christians running a race, we have a cloud of witnesses as the Bible puts it; these people have been here before: people like Abraham, Moses, Elijah, John, Paul, Esther, Job, my grandmother and many more. It is worthy to note that because they were not defeated, they are now seated in heavenly places as examples for us who are still in the race. So we call these guests *a crowd,* who would be coming on this day as your earthly witnesses. No matter how big or small a crowd is, a crowd is still a crowd. Just for curiosity's sake, is it going to be a large crowd or a small one?

Both of you must have discussed this before now and agreed on the number of people coming. Agreement over every issue is of critical importance when you are in a relationship. You are no longer expected to do things the way you used to when it was you alone. You submit one to another; submitting to one another means respecting ideas, buying into the dreams, visions and aspirations, correcting in love and objectively criticising each other. In so doing, you are working in agreement. It is only when you walk in agreement that you invoke the presence of the Lord; remember, '*if two of you shall agree concerning a thing, it shall be done*'. You do not want to shut God out. Agreement also opens the door to trust, respect, and understanding. *Can two walk together unless they agree?* How do you agree over a thing? You agree by effective communication; telling her how you feel at any given time and listening to her feedback. Always stop and listen. Listening is the core element of effective communication. There is no point talking to her and moving away without hearing her own version of the story. Even if she is walking out while you are still talking, which some men do when they cannot stand the heat of intense conversation, keep talking Son.

She is not a man though, and so she won't walk out. I believe that she will listen to you. Devise a means to always communicate with her, my dear Son. You can call her on the phone, send her text messages, drop her little notes on the fridge, slip a note into her work lunch bag, in the bathroom or just anywhere she can see the note. Always remember that communication is a two-way thing; it's a conversation, a dialogue not a monologue and if you have conveyed your message to your recipient and not gotten a response, you have not achieved anything. Communicate with your five senses and with your body. Present your body as a sacrifice to her; always speak positive things and using gentle touch to comfort and to reassure her. Let her find kindness in the comfort of your eyes. Does this not remind you of God? When we communicate with Him through our prayers, He hears us and He speaks back to us. He understands us and knows our mind. Little wonder He said, *'come and let us reason together'*. This means, come let's have a conversation; come let us communicate. If you don't bend your knees, God cannot stretch his hands; so it is a joint effort between God and us. You play your part and God plays His part. You never liked me talking to my friends or even to anyone on the phone for what you considered *too long*. As a child, you always came to distract my conversations. I remember cutting people off from the phone just to attend to my Son. I can tell you now that not every person will tolerate that. No matter what trash they are conversing about, you must allow them to finish. This is going to apply to your wife-to-be when she comes to live with you. She is a girl and will love to have *a girl-talk* with her friends or even her sisters. Just make sure you do not rush her on the phone or stand in front of her, as you often did to me to ask her for something which you know can wait until the phone conversations are over.

Back to the crowd issue; regarding the number of people coming for the wedding, do not be afraid of any size of crowd. Just have the attitude of

Jesus who hosted a large crowd in the Bible. He welcomed them, touched them, held their babies in his arms and fed them with only two fish and five loaves of bread and guess what, there was still a surplus at the end. Whatever you can provide on that day, simply give thanks and serve it to them. We have more than enough in our Father's house and there is always an abundance of supply in his presence. The Lord will increase and multiply your refreshments on that day; you will see. You will be surprised that not only will they be well fed, there will also be surplus. Jesus demonstrated that it does not matter how much resources we have at hand, all we need is a heart of gratitude. God is our source of supply and He supplies all our needs according to his riches in glory through Christ Jesus. Just remember, *to whom much is given, much is required.* I wonder what you will choose to do with the surplus. Could it go to the homeless people on the streets? That is called mission in a book '*The purpose driven life*', the book we studied as a group in the house for four weeks. It is called ministry when you meet the needs of people in the house of God and mission when you step out in faith to minister to people who are outside the fold. You can give them to the dogs. That's not a bad idea as the book of Proverbs says that *a good man cares for his animals*. You can minister to the environment by recycling it. Some people don't really care about our planet for some strange reasons best known to them; some for political reasons and some out of sheer ignorance. But you have to care because God hates waste. He picks up all the leftovers because he knows how to put them to good use. That has been our idea in the house. Anyway, those are my ways. I am not sure if anyone will be similar minded in your generation. What do you think Jesus did with the leftovers? If we are to go by His words, the little boy who provided the refreshments would have received the leftovers. For the boy, those twelve leftover baskets became the harvest for his seed. The leftovers became his miracle for caring to bring and to give.

'How do you know mum?'

'Well, God always multiplies.'

He does Son. Don't forget the offering song we used to sing on Sundays, although sometimes these become routines and lose their meaning but they are true and alive.

The song says:

Give and it shall be given unto you; good measure, pressed down, shaken together and running over.....

Never impose your ideas on your spouse; always prayerfully agree on an issue before you carry out a plan, for this is the only way forward. I know you saved a good amount of money for the occasion but have you agreed on a budget yet with her and are you two working by the budget? I really do not want to sound like that old worrisome woman called mother that you have always known. I am only trying to help out. I taught you how to make to-do lists and you learnt from all your teachers how to keep a journal. Make use of the memos in your mobile phone, paste them on the door to your room, on your fridge or office door, bathroom door, write things down on your palm when you remember them and you have no writing materials but I am sure that you will have something to write on at all times. I taught you that a long time ago. This letter should serve as a reminder or whatever you want to call it. Always keep it with you. Let it not depart from your sight, so that you can have a good wedding. Ponder on these.

Have you made your lists yet? Or are the planners going to handle everything for you? Whatever the case is, you still need to have your own lists, even things as small as confetti and the first dance song. Harking back to our first dance now, I can still clearly visualise how your dad held me in his arms with those reassuring looks and how he zoomed off afterwards to do his *dodgy* dancing. Anyway, tick off the things that you have given attention to. Know your priorities and things you can do without, in case it comes to that. The lists are always endless but here are a few things I can think about now: the invites, the venues, photographers, florists, caterers, musicians, master of ceremony and chauffeurs. Remember that invitations are spread far beyond your friends and colleagues. Thank God you are getting married in this city, which means that no one has to travel from afar. If you had planned to do it abroad, you would have needed to arrange for accommodation, childcare, airport pickups, and possibly cultural or leisure activities for the comfort and entertainment of your guests but I am so delighted you did not go that route.

Son, by now you know how much I hate that monster called procrastination, which you are used to and worse still, your dad. I like to get things done ahead of time to avoid anxiety when the time comes and that was the reason why I called you www.*lastminuteman.home* when you were a child. I am pretty sure that you have changed a whole lot now. If you have anything to do, just get up and do it, do not wait until the next minute or the next day. Remember what the Bible says: *'a little sleep, a little slumber and poverty comes knocking at your door'*. Poverty, I am absolutely sure is not in God's plan for you, so don't bring it upon yourself. That is the reason why He said in His Word: *'be ye transformed by the renewing of your mind'*. You will have a different frame of mind. Even when you are tired, you will gain strength from within. You will say it like you already have it and up you'll get. *Let he that is weak say: 'I am strong'*. Think about it. If you don't get up on time, you could lose your job because you would always be late for work and if you don't work you will not eat and subsequently you will die. God does not provide manna for people these days like He did in the past; the days for that kind of miracle are gone. Therefore, He wants you to get your lazy backside up from that chair and do something with your life. Anyway,

I know that you can do better than that. So those days are gone when you use to stay in bed until everyone else had gotten up. You did that more on school days, nearly every morning and when you woke up, you moaned about how you did not get a good night's sleep. Meanwhile, for me to get you to bed on time was often nearly a *mission impossible*. That is the time when you would remember to drink water, get your stuff from downstairs or remember the homework journal I did not sign earlier. When you eventually got out of bed in the morning, you would start one argument or another with your brothers. You were shockingly funny. I remember asking you one morning why you did not sleep well the previous night and you told me that the window was slightly open. I asked why you didn't get up to close the window and you said that getting up from your bed (which was just an inch away) would make you stay awake longer than you had been. Yet you ended up not sleeping all night. That was really hilarious! I knew you made that up because that was one of the numerous excuses you gave every morning when you wanted to get a little more time in bed.

I knew somehow that we would hold this conversation someday and if I may ask, why was it difficult? Despite all the motivations I gave you, you were bent on doing things your own way. Getting up early was really tough for you. I tried so many things that did not work but only God knew how we managed through those years. The idea of natural consequences did not work so much. When your dad bought an alarm clock, all you did was quietly turned it off and lie back to sleep. You hated making your bed so much that most times I would let you go to school knowing that if you didn't make your bed in the morning, you had to do it first thing when you got back from school or else there would be no treat. I learnt that on time. You were all that Son and the times you would wake up early were only the days you were going on school trips. A day to that day, you would be early to bed and follow all the instructions to a *'T'*. You allowed temporary things like going on a school trip to be your motivation for getting up early. On such occasions, you would get up first and start getting ready for school. God help your mum if you were going to go with no uniforms, which means a change of clothes as was usually the case. Like the wicked, no one in the house would have peace until you were gone and back, with half of the things you went with forgotten on the bus or swapped with someone else out of excitement. So one trip that would have taken other people one day, would take our whole family three days. We had to call the school just to make sure that your things were where you said you left them, so that another child would not take them home until the next time you were in school.

Thank God you are different now. In fact, we are all different – we are all a bunch of *can-do* people, who can do all things now through Christ who strengthens us. *All things* include taking care of our things and getting up early to do things. By the way, you have to wake up early to do devotions before you head out of that house, whether it be personal or between you and your spouse. It could also be in the night like we do; whichever works better for you but it is important you do that because that is exactly where this strength I am talking about comes from. Remember, *they that wait on the Lord shall renew their strength.* This means strength to do things that you ordinarily will be unable to do on your own.

In those days, you lacked the strength to do lots of things; expecting your brothers always to go get a bath first, brush their teeth first and more because
'I got a bath first yesterday,
I watered the plants yesterday,
I made the bed yesterday'.

You would expect your brothers to take care of everything for the rest of the week because you did something once on one day of the week. I hope you truly know by now that you cannot do that. Just remember, you have to face up to your responsibilities and challenges as a man and do not leave them for anyone else. Other people, as you already know by now, have their own issues to deal with. Try to do as much as you can when you can do them, with what you have and for whom the Lord has given you. Talking about responsibilities, I really have to leave this letter now and go prepare your brother's dinner. He will be flying in today from England and your dad will be picking him up from the airport. You know how hungry you boys can get the moment you step into this house. While growing up, you always told me that when you start earning money, you would buy lots of fast foods from McDonalds and Burger King. What made you to change your mind? Your brother in particular once told your dad and I that once he's grown up and made lots of money, he would buy only fast food, as he hated my cooking. He complained that it looked too proper for his junk craving appetite. Sure I know, *when I was a child, I spoke like a child, I reasoned like a child and when I grew up, I gave up childish thinking*. He really gave it up. Tell me, how come you started to like my food? You guys made me feel that my food could not be given to a dog! You used to cry nearly every time you came back from school in those days:

Rice again?,

Pasta again?,

Potatoes again?,

oh! Mum not 'Garri',

You acted as though these were poisons and most times you had to be bribed to eat them. The worst was when they were served with fruit or vegetables. I remember you as a child telling me that you were a vegetarian; that you don't eat vegetables; you were funny, you know. You and your brother drove me crazy over fruit and vegetables. I stopped at nothing to get you to eat them. I am not talking about the efforts made by your school. The National School then had a project they called *food campaign*, which was fruitful while it lasted. You were even in the school food committee. You would come home boasting and showing off all the treats and gifts that came with that campaign – plastic plates and drinking cans which were given to you guys as gifts. Unfortunately, your interest could not be sustained beyond the life of that project. On my part, I was advised not to force you to eat them, rather to gradually talk you into eating them. I watched and listened to so many people and viewed programmes on how to prepare vegetables and fruit. I was asked not to overcook them; sometimes I applied different methods of cooking. Your dad used to buy a box of fruit and *veggies* every Saturday morning on his way from work. So as soon as we woke up I would make *smoothies* with them, remember? I used to serve the vegetables with peanut butter and mayonnaise, especially when I cut varieties of vegetables and served them in a wide tray, which you liked so much. Sometimes adding a seasoning blend, just to get you to eat them. Sammy's mum, our next door neighbour then told me that she gets Sammy involved in meal planning, shopping, cooking and that the moment Sammy identified the *veggies* and participated in choosing and cooking them for dinner, he started to eat them. I decided to do that with you. I remember taking you to the shop to select your choices of fruit and vegetables. You and your brothers were so busy trying to build a masterpiece structure out of the fruit and *veggies*; I was so discouraged that I ended up coming home with my choices. I tried on many occasions to encourage you, telling you that like the Word of God which says, the '*fruit of the Spirit*' helps us to grow in the Lord, fruit and veggies will help you grow strong and healthy. John the Minister teaches us in Church about the fruit of the Spirit. One Sunday, he came to church with fruit and *veggies* and he jokingly asked us which fruit comes to church every week. No one but Philip answered the question right. Surprisingly it was *Lettuce*. What a nice joke to crack in the house of the Lord. *'Lettuce' (let us pray)!* Sure he has a knack for telling holy jokes. Everyone tried everything to get you to appreciate healthy diet. Even my mentor, Michelle Obama, with all her White House arsenal of warheads and heavy machineries of *'let's move'* and *home grown green'* effects could not have worked on your cravings for junk food if she was our neighbour. Thank goodness, *'when knowledge came, his eyes opened.'* Little wonder the Bible says that *'in the day of His power, His people shall be willing.'* No longer shall a man say to his brother *'know the Lord.'* God manifested His power to your brother through His knowledge and the power of this knowledge gave him ability, willingness and strength to change his lifestyle.

Anyway, I told you that I am preparing dinner for your brother. He has already ordered what he wants – a lot of vegetables in his food and fruit as dessert; no more ice cream and cake. Dear Son, can you believe that your mum is now your brother's student, he now educates me on the importance of healthy eating. The last time he was here, he told your dad and I how the

World Health Organisation estimated that 2.7 million lives would be spared if people simply ate fruit and vegetables. He regretted knowing it late and remembered how he hated lots of fruit and *veggies* and suffered functional constipation as a child. He told me that if he knew earlier, it wouldn't have happened to him because it would have simply been a matter of eating right. Then he wouldn't have gone through the pain of trying to use the toilet and possibly wouldn't have gone through those courses of medication I used to give him. Just listen to this – he told me that my eye problem was due to the fact that I did not eat as much fruit and vegetables as I claimed to have eaten when I was a child and that if I really had done so, the antioxidants in the fruit and *veggies* would have prevented my eyes from getting bad. What can I say? I really don't blame him as I am the one who accepted the role of the student in the first place and he, as my teacher was therefore given the privilege of tutoring me. You know your mother son, I did not waste time in expressing to him that a number of factors can exacerbate health conditions; not only lifestyle or ancestral genes but most of all, environmental degradation. I recognize that and can't be fooled or deceived by your brother's late-learning exuberance. That is by the way as I am delighted to have him spend the weekend with us. I really don't mind him using me to improve on his teaching skills, after all I am always a well-mannered student and you know that.

The mood in the house will be a much happier one. The last time I had you two was at my grandmother's memorial service. I miss my grandmother so much as she was such fun to be with. You were only two when you saw her last and she held you for the two hours when we were at her house and wouldn't let go of you. Grandma was the best; she was very strong and energetic. She was simply like Jesus; honestly I used to think as a child that she must be related to Jesus, no wonder she acted and behaved like him.

I remember one day that I did something terribly bad at home and as the custom of the house then was, you would expect a good smacking when dad returned. So when my dad came home and was told what I did, I was terrified as I watched him go to get his cane. The moment he turned towards me, I jetted off to grandma's apartment. Dad followed me as I ran and you need to see the rage on his face. I thought it was the end for me. As he got closer, I dived behind grandma and could have entered under her skirt. Grandma quickly stretched out her two arms drawing a picture of Jesus on the cross when he came to redeem us. She said; *kill me first, before you get to her.* I will never forget that statement as long as I live. My dad looked at her sternly as though he was asking the question: *you again*? Then he said, 'have you asked her what she did?' Grandma replied, 'whatever she did does not warrant you chasing her into my house with that long stick and in that mood'. That thing you have in your hand is not going to undo anything she has done.

Do you know that from Grandma's back where I was hiding, I was relieved and was thinking *yes! I am free at last*. That is one of the reasons why Grandma reminds me so much about God and His divine grace. Although my dad had the best of intentions - to discipline me but I wonder if his approach was the most effective. But my grandmother understood the meaning of grace *(undeserved favour)* and became the Jesus I needed at that moment. God is always willing to shield you from any trouble or danger as his child, irrespective of what you have done. His first duty is to accept you and protect you before any other thing. No wonder Jesus said: '*as many as come to my Father, He will in no wise cast them out'*, whatever the offence.

Grandma helped my mum to raise us, as mum was her only daughter and she wouldn't let her go through raising us alone. She was always there for everyone and she cooked like a chef that was imported from heaven. I still remember that her favourite food was beans and corn. She had a special way of making them. My grandma was a typical example of how Christian women should live their lives as her straightforward demeanour was very refreshing. She never spoke when she was angry, never lost her temper with us or anyone, she was always meditating on the Bible and consistently praying – she told us that prayer was the key to everything in life. She did not condone any derogatory language from anyone in her family. Timothy in the Bible had such a Grandma who taught him everyday, the good things he knew and in fact, Timothy's record was that he knew everything that was written in the Bible from childhood.

I recall sitting with Grandma and listening to her tell me stories of when her kids were young and what she went through to raise them. To feed them, according to her, she had to wake up very early, three days a week before the cock crowed to look for bargains from a big market which was located some distance away from home. In this market she bought articles and re-sold them to people who were too lazy to travel and use the proceeds to feed her children. She would make a little profit that enabled her to buy other necessities for her family. She told of how she was woken up in the mornings by the crowing cock and the ringing Church bell. She was not particularly familiar with the clock, not that she could not read a clock, no, but it was a waste of time. The cock was more reliable than the clock. Another more reliable thing than the clock was the church morning prayer bell. There was the first and the second bell. The morning prayer bell rang even before the cock crowed. Latecomers to the morning prayers were tolerated only after the first bell but not after the second one. So she would normally go to the church for morning prayers before going to the market. In those stories that she told, she said that on one of the mornings, the church catechist came to unlock the church to ring the bell. The catechist, she would explain was the person who assisted the main minister in the church with minor duties. So as he came to unlock the door that morning, he saw a vision of the angels getting ready to write down the names of people who came early to pray. In the hands of the angels were gifts wrapped in parcel-like manners. According to grandmas' description, the gifts were wrapped in banana leaves and tied up with strips of palm frond leaves in ribbon-like forms. The first few people that came received the gifts. 'Were you one of them Grandma?' I remembered asking her. She would always give a weak smile after which I would ask her to start the same story from the beginning with the hope that she might accept that she did receive a gift. I would then ask her what the gift was. Grandma, as we all knew her, could never go to any of God's meetings late. She would always tell you that from that experience the church catechist had, the angels always wrote down the names of early comers and that she didn't want to miss out on God's blessings. I think that was a true vision, because it sounds like what God would do. He likes faithfulness and diligence.

People are faithful and diligent when they experience the love of God and realise how much they mean to Him. He does not compel or police us but He rewards those who diligently seek him. That story affected my service to God. If you could recall, I would rather stay back home than go to church or any meeting late. You would always ask for another minute to use the bathroom or pick up *something* from your room when it was time to leave the house and most often we arrived late because of such. Some people don't even care, mainly because they do not understand. In fact they would want to come in slapping their high heeled shoes on the hard floor when others are trying to meditate or pray, just to draw attention to themselves. I don't know how that is consideration or love for a neighbour, if you cannot allow him that time of meditation. I may be wrong. A couple of years ago, if it strikes a chord, the minister spoke about the issue of coming to church late and some people in the church volunteered to become ushers, workers or greeters, whatever you want to call them, the work of those greeters was to stop the latecomers by the door in a gentle manner, at least until the prayer time was over.

Grandma was married to a polygamist, who left his wives to fend for themselves and their children. He cared little about how the women and his children were fed and clothed; they even had to fix their leaking roofs by themselves. This was not a very good experience for her. He would then turn around to boast of how hard-working his wives were; how very rich they had made him and how many children they had for him – children whose names he sometimes could not even remember. I still recall how you would open your eyes very wide to listen to this story and wondered how one man could be married to so many women and have dozens of children. I would say 'yes it is very true. True of certain titled men in Africa where we come from'. These men believe that marrying many wives would bring them more wealth, more children and probably more pleasure and fulfillment. It is true that some religions allow this – claiming that God allowed men to marry up to four wives. Those who support these ideas believe that as men are killed in wars, there would be more women than men. As a result, there would not be enough men to match the number of women wanting to get married. So the practice of polygamy was intended to curb adultery as every woman would have a husband and a name attached to her no matter how many women were already married to the same man. According to them, this whole arrangement leads to happier marriages and fewer divorces. Now you are a grown man, how true is it that a man can love more than one woman and show them equal love? I think it is one of man's numerous ways of playing God and trying to be what he can never be. I never heard Grandma talk about a love relationship between herself and her husband, no, in this case their husband. I don't think any of their children experienced the same one-on-one love, care and attention we got from our dad and you from your dad. But how could that be, when their dad could not even recall their first names sometimes; and a situation where their mums had to play the role of both dad and mum at the same time. This experience can also be applied to men who kept concubines as they were called in those days or mistresses now. You know the truth now: God designed marriage to be between one man and one woman; my Bible tells me. These men lacked understanding; no wonder they wallowed in ignorance but they should be grateful to God that such things as *STD's* were not very common then. They could have infected good people like Grandma who happened to find herself in this web. Up until now, I do not know if that was by choice, although the common saying then was that a man is the husband of all. She told me how she would travel on foot for miles to the farm with her children and when they got back, they would eat in a hurry so as to take the crops to the market to sell. She proudly told us how the money she made was able to send mum and her two younger brothers to school and how she worked very hard until dad came to ask for mum's hand in marriage. In a way it was a relief, she said smiling; a relief to know that someone whom she saw as noble had come to marry her only daughter and promised to send her to school to finish her primary education in the big city. That automatically meant that she would one day arrange to bring her two younger brothers to the city and help them get better education also. So that was how my mum was married off.

Shortly afterwards, civil war broke out in our country and mum told us that Grandma relinquished everything including her last life savings and her *white horse bike* to make sure that they were alright. White horse bikes were very rare in her village then and according to Grandma, she was one of the first people to own one. So when the war broke out, there was scarcity of food and the little available was very expensive. Kids died of malnutrition and she had no option than to sell off that luxury bike. I am very sure you remember the Biafran war; that war that your dad is so passionate about whenever he told the story. According to my mum, they had lost everything they owned and it was very difficult for them to even feed. Mum was left to care for her little children as dad was drafted into the army to help build guns and he had to move from one area to another. This meant that he was hardly ever home. It would have been a hopeless situation if not for Grandma, your great-grandmother.

She was indeed a woman of faith and godly character. I miss her but heaven gained. I can't believe I still talk about her with misty eyes, although it has been a long time since she left. Her memory still lingers and every good woman I come across reminds me of her. Grandma was present during my marriage to your dad and I remember her earnestly praying for us for hours unending. She sang and danced. In fact at one time I thought that she was drunk but she was not. That was Grandma for you especially when she was in a worshipful or merry mood. You remember the old Bible that was always by my bedside? That was Grandmas' wedding gift for me. Oh, how so sweet. She will always be remembered. Because of Grandma, I eagerly wanted to be a wife, then a mother and a grandmother. Though some of the children from these polygamous homes claim to be one big happy family, they don't really seem to know the differences between what they have and what other children have. I often wondered if children from these polygamous homes really believe their claims, because I felt that the contrariety was too glaring to be overlooked. I could not even imagine exchanging the life I knew for what they had. They claim to cook and eat from one pot, share clothes and even bedrooms. According to them, the children respect all the mothers and addressed each one of their dad's wives as mum. I saw lots of these families as we grew up with kids from them and played together as friends.

I had always wanted to have my own children and care for them the way Grandma cared for her children and her grandchildren. I prayed to God to give me a good man and a good family, God answered that prayer.

I know what you are thinking about now, but sorry I am not going there. I have this feeling that the next thing you will want me to recount is how your dad and I met. I know you guys loved to hear that story a lot. You never got tired of listening to the story as often as it was told. I remember your brother asking me one day when he was nine, *mum, so when was the first kiss?* I am not telling you that story again in this letter but can I still remind you that God directed and ordered our footsteps and our paths crossed. You cannot be directed if you do not have the spirit of God and when you have his spirit, you will be led and will remain in his presence.

My concept of marriage is that anyone who is ready for marriage should prayerfully find their marriage partner and negotiate that by themselves. I can never be a sister to Hagar, who fixed a marriage for her son Ishmael in the wilderness. I don't live in the wilderness and you are not a weak child who is not capable of doing things other children your age do for themselves. I am also not an in-law to Mrs Bennett, the lady in the book *Pride and Prejudice*, who was out to arrange relationships straightaway for her daughters. She did that whenever the wealthy and the noble were in town. Just remember, that in every arrangement, there are always terms and conditions attached. It sounds like this: I will do this for you because or if you will do that for me. If you scratch my back, then I'll scratch your back. When trouble comes, you would then remember the person who arranged the marriage and blame them. But the story is different when you find a wife yourself; more so with God's guidance. You have the ability to face the challenges that come with it. You don't blame anyone rather you turn to God. Such a relationship is usually based on unconditional love, the kind of love that God has for us. I am also on the beam that these days, people are thrilled to search for marriage partners on the internet and from newspapers. Whether it works for them or not, is another matter. There has always been a pattern of behaviour for people who truly want to obey the Lord and to do His will. The patriarchs, as we read in the Bible, always saw or met their wives at the well. Could that mean the presence of the Lord by interpretation? I do not know but that was their pattern. One thing I know is that you must look within the parameters of the Word of God. Nothing, absolutely nothing less than that is acceptable. For if you don't, you will be taking a casual trip, like Sampson did to Timnath. Sampson's parents asked him, 'Son, is there no woman among the daughters of thy brethren or among all our people that you could take for a wife?' They did not support Sampson as experience had taught them that women from outside their people had little truth in them –they were deceptive and full of lies. Judah was deceived by his own daughter in-law, as she lived a lie. She was a Timnath. Therefore they knew that they did not have the truth in them. Time proved them right when the women in Sampson's life who were also from Timnath, the land of the Philistines showed their true colours. It is important to note here that Timnath is no longer a geographical location, rather a relationship without the Lord.

I have always advised you to pray and fast from the beginning. You must fast when you are ready to look, so that your mind will be focused and be in tune with God as you communicate with him. The fear of the Lord brings wisdom. I have also asked you to be watchful so as to recognise the deceptions of the devil. The devil always presents beautiful outward packages that are nothing close to what they really are on the inside. I remember telling you that you must open your eyes to see a level of consistency in any girl concerning her love for the things of God. First, she has to be a committed Christian who loves and fears the Lord; remember, *by their fruits, you will know them*. Anyone who truly believes must produce the fruits of righteousness. Although there is a human limit to what we can see, the Lord sees right through the heart. Therefore we must wait on Him for direction. Son, if you follow these steps, just know that you are on the right track and you can never go wrong.

It gives me much joy when I remember the way you felt the first time you told me about this girl. I have seen you tickled pink when you got new toys as a child, during your school trips, graduation and when you got your first job. You love technology, forever looking to acquire the latest gadgets and you were always one of the first to queue up, even through the night to get a new iPhone and stuff like that. Then you would describe it and the way you felt owning it. In your excitement you would go on endlessly about your new acquisition to the annoyance of everyone around you. Things you saw from trips abroad were always fascinating and you spoke about them like someone who had just visited the moon. But as a matter of fact, I never saw that level of excitement with combined shyness in your eyes, something in your spirit softened and relaxed, there was a twinkle in your eyes which I had never seen before then. You have never described anything in your life the way you described this girl. I remember that evening, how you gently put down the cup of tea that I had made for you on the coffee table next to me and moved closer. This was your pattern during those years whenever you wanted to ask for something special or when you got into trouble and would not want your dad to know about it but this time you explained to me that you were neither asking for anything nor were you in trouble. You only wanted me to feel and share in your excitements. In that usual quiet but deep voice you said:

'Mum.'

'Yes Son.'

'You will marvel.'

'Marvel at what?'

'You will soon see her.'

'See who?'

'You will soon see her, mum,
Believe me she is like the daughter you never had.
You will definitely love her.'

Still staring at you and completely puzzled, I tried to figure out what you were trying to tell me and looking into those excited eyes of yours that spoke more than your mouth, I asked:

'Love who?'

You said: 'Mum, she is absolutely beautiful, delightful and charming, her eyes are as soft and as single as that of a dove. She is so gentle and kind. She's got virtues; she's got brains and a good education. She's got class, she's got manners and above all, she's got God'. You sat there repeating yourself over and over again. There and then I knew that to a degree something had happened to my son. I knew that you had finally found love, a soul mate, the bone of your bones and the flesh of your flesh. I quickly remembered what Solomon wrote in the Song of Songs:

'Love flashes like fire,
The brightest kind of flame,
Many waters cannot quench love,
Neither can rivers drown it'.

I waited until you left to really thank the Lord my God the way I love to and the way the Most High loves it. I expressed my heartfelt gratitude to Him for giving you direction and wisdom to look beyond human eyes. Son, you know the way I praise Him,
I lift my hands up,
I bow down,
I kneel down,
I lie flat on my belly and I scream down the house.
I don't really care who was listening or watching,

although I hate to be distracted. When I praise the Lord in songs, I praise him until I am very sure that the Lord has accepted my sacrifice of praise. I sing and dance before His presence until I am sure that He has gotten up from His throne and He is set in train to dance to my sweet melodies. I make sure that the angels in heaven have also become part of my praises. I remember one day when I was in this mood of praise. You and your brother walked in and you were a bit scared. Your brother said: 'Come on, we must find it.'

'Find what', you asked him.

'The drink of course.'

He honestly thought that I had been drinking. At the end of my communion with the Lord I explained to you two that I was not drunk with wine, rather I was drunk in the Holy Ghost. That same day I read to you the book of the Acts of the Apostles, when on the day of Pentecost, the Spirit of the Lord came and filled the apostles with the anointing. They spoke in different tongues; the people around the disciples were amazed and they thought that they were drunk. Peter, who was also filled with the Holy Spirit got up and explained that rare experience to them. What about the woman in the Old Testament called Hannah, the mother of Samuel? Hannah was troubled and she went to the presence of the Lord to have communion with Him. While she was still there, I am sure that she did not care about who was looking at her, like your mum would not care, she did not even notice the high priest himself. That high priest was nothing compared to our present High Priest, who understands our every move, every emotion, every situation and can be touched by them. So the high priest thought that she was drunk. 'I am not', replied Hannah; 'I have drunk neither wine nor strong drink'

The love and joy we find in the presence of God when we seek Him and worship Him with all our hearts can be quite intoxicating. Consequently I was not surprised that day when your first inclination was to look for an empty bottle of wine. When you go into the presence of the Lord, Son, you have freedom, you have boldness, you express yourself the way you would to your loved one, to someone with whom you have an intimate relationship with. Very soon Son, you will discover what I really mean. You are not ashamed to be associated with God when you are a child of His, because you know exactly who he is and what he stands for. I remember king David was like that when the Ark of the Covenant was on its way to Jerusalem after a long time in a strange land. David danced and danced until his wife was concerned and was almost ashamed of him. Sometimes people around you don't understand that feeling and experience. There is fullness of joy in the presence of the Lord. Sometimes I wonder why people cannot give an ordinary smile in the gathering of the people of God. In the company of such people, you can feel some kind of weight and unexplained heaviness, which can be infectious if you let them. So I really blessed the name of the Lord when you left, I also thanked the Lord for the joy and the peace that came with that piece of information as I reveled in the thought of becoming a mother-in-law and soon by His grace a grandmother. Although I refused to dwell so much on that, I am convinced that I will make a good one. At the end, I felt this strange but welcome feeling of being young again.

You were right Son, that first day you brought her over, the moment she walked through that door, I marveled just like you predicted. I was thrilled by her confident looks and good manners. She wore a very cheerful face that made her irresistible. She looked very magnificent, adorable and amiable. For the first few minutes, I was in awe; no, that is not the right word, I still really cannot describe with words exactly how I felt the moment she walked in, until she left. When I looked down and saw her beautiful feet; there and then I concluded that she was complete *good news; the best kept secret*. It was then I remembered what my mum used to say, that if you want to know a beautiful girl, look at her from her legs down.

I did that Son.

When I looked up to her face one more time, she looked like the work of a skilled craftsman. She is the most gorgeous looking girl I had ever seen. There was something about her that was quite distinctive. At first glance, I noticed the expressions on her face which radiated peace, joy, goodness, gentleness, beauty and every good thing you could think about. She was so dark and beautiful, her long dark braided hair which she packed behind revealed her strikingly beautiful and bold brown eyes. Her teeth were as white as sheep, with no gaps, perfect in every part. I had never seen such a beauty.

She is indeed a beauty to behold. You two, in fact, would make a perfect couple. You are also kind, so gentle and loving; you are good looking and strong, your arms are like round bars of gold and your legs are strong like pillars of marble set in sockets of the finest gold, strong as the cedars of Lebanon. Your smile Son, can bring reassurance to any woman.

No wonder it took you that long to find her. I remember you told your brother how difficult it was for you to get her to even look at you. It was very hard for her to accept you as a friend, despite the fact that all the girls that ever came across you the first time wanted you for a husband immediately. You actually saw her before she saw you; and chose her before you knew her; you did not know anything about her family background, her academic background, her ugly past or her bank account. Little wonder you stopped at nothing to get her. That whisper of the spirit you heard in your soul made you to pursue her as your destiny and the strength of that voice and the knowledge that His word is *yeah and amen* caused you to win. Yes, I can recall that you said you sought her for months. At first she did not seem to have noticed you and when she did, she bluffed you. Not surprising, like so many girls who know their worth, she did not come running to you at the wave of your hand. Girls like that would really want to know exactly who you are and exactly what you want from them. They have purpose and mission in life. They are eager to find a man who has a vision and a focus; one with a purpose and a good sense of direction. They want an honest and godly friendship first, as any other thing is only spoken word.

It is only in a relationship that you get revelations. Your person would be revealed to them by God. Such girls do not want to have anything done in the dark and they have respect for God and for themselves. I was like that with your dad. It is called a woman's pride and love for God. I had a woman's pride and your dad to date, still respects me for that.

When this started, if you could recall, I was not informed. I overheard you the day you were talking with your brother in the hallway about it. Usually you guys never discussed such things with me until there is little trouble; so I waited till then. Although I will forever wonder why, despite all the love and affection I showed, you only chose to open up when there were problems. You are boys; yes I agree but I opened up to you more than any mum would open up to their daughters. Anyway, on that particular day I was glad when I overheard your brother encouraging you to fight on and never to give up; his exact words were *fight to win her over*. Suddenly, I heard that phrase and I honestly thought that you were having a row with someone; so when I finally understood the conversation, I screamed *yes* in my mind. To be honest, my laundry basket nearly fell off my hands because the joy I caught from that single phrase, *fight to win her over*, was much. It had lots of meanings to me. I was overjoyed as I pondered over those words, realising that something was in the making. Perhaps to you, it was timely and an eye opener that transformed your thoughts. That was not the first time you heard that sort of phrase anyway. It could also mean to persevere, to hold on, to keep on, to linger, endure and stay on. I guess that was the understanding you ran with and I am very sure that you raised your standards and tactics a little higher. What did you really do in your perseverance? Did you buy her cards or did you make her one, like your dad often did for me? I remember he sent me lots of very colourful handmade cards then and each time his envelope arrived in the post, my roommates admired them intensely. As if that was not enough, they talked about the cards so much outside the room that my schoolmates came to my room, just to see the latest one. He also wrote me lots of poems. So what did you do? Did you send her flowers? Did you get her lunch at break times or did you get a makeover just for her to notice you? If so, it must have been an extreme makeover. Hmmm! Just a word of advice, when both of you are finally married, do not get tired of doing such things. They call it *spicing up* a marriage relationship. Some husbands don't remember to do such things anymore; they only wait till Valentine's Day and thereafter, love takes a back seat till the next year.

After that conversation, it was not very long before you came running back to your brother screaming *yes, you were right after all, it worked*. As God would have it, I heard this follow-up conversation and once again, I rejoiced exceedingly. But can I ask you how come you didn't know that you cannot get something that good so easily? Why did that word *perseverance* not mean much to you all those years? Your dad and I drummed it into your ears – well I guess in God's time He makes all things beautiful. I remember you cried over the boy that defeated you at the library chess competition every Saturday; you would always come second to him and sometimes third and I always adviced you to *persist, keep trying*. I told you times without number that *practice makes perfect*. You really practiced; you regularly played with your brothers at home and you felt so upset by those defeats that you asked only for a game of chess that year for a birthday present. I never knew there was a chess game on the Internet but you discovered that. So that very day as I came to collect you after a chess club meeting, you ran to me and almost pushed me down because you had beaten that champ that gave you a tough time all along. You beat him Son, with that word *'perseverance'*. From that day, you and the other chess mates had peace as he no longer bragged at your face. That was your first significant victory and it lasted you a while.

The story is quite similar to that of David and Goliath, you remember. You loved that story so much and you were never bored hearing it. Sometimes the children are told stories in Sunday school but they don't understand them. People don't understand things when they don't mix them with faith. Sometimes they think it is one of those Spiderman, Superman or Power Ranger stories. Yes Son, there was a way you particularly looked at those Bible stories and I could not blame you. At that time, it was probably the stage you were at. I remember one day, John our Church minister told the story of Zacchaeus the small man, who heard that Jesus was coming and all that he could do was to quickly climb up the tree in order to see Jesus. It was in the middle of the story that you pointed out to John to please ask Zacchaeus to come down, because if he does not come down quickly he would come down crashing and his skull might break into pieces. It was funny but the funniest was one Christmas when John was explaining what Santa had in his bag when he visits the kids at Christmas. He spoke about the significance of them, like the angel, the star, the gifts and the rest of them. Then he went on to bring out things from his Santa's bag and apologised that he was unable like Santa to fit the Christmas tree in that one bag. So he brought in the tree earlier. Son, you raised your hand in the middle of the Church service and said to the minister, 'Sir, if you ever come across Santa, would you tell him to come with a bigger bag next time so that everything will be in one bag'. That was hilarious and no one could stop laughing that day.

You were a normal kid and most times kids give different interpretations and meanings to the words they hear. I got that understanding as a Sunday school teacher. I never failed to pray for all the children I taught, presenting them before the Lord at all times. To be honest, it is not always fun teaching someone if they fail to understand. It does not give teachers joy and if understanding comes from God, then I have to ask Him to give it to them. As the children's Sunday-school teacher, praying for understanding for them is my responsibility. This also applies to teachers of adults; you really have to pray for the adults you are teaching so that their eyes of understanding would be enlightened, like Paul prayed for his students in the Bible. It is not just praying for them; you really have to plan your lessons and prepare your topics well and then think of an appropriate approach. This is how to introduce a topic. Do fair amounts of research, put in good and quality amount of time to prepare, compare notes and finally scale it down to the level of your students understanding. You have instructed others before, so I know you understand exactly what I am talking about.

Regarding the chess, you really made me proud, the same way we make God proud when we persevere and overcome the trials and temptations that challenge our faith. It wasn't your brother or any other person who fought that fight in winning your bride over. In the same way, God will be there watching you as you overcome subsequent challenges that may come your way. Once in a while, He might send an angel to reposition you but He does not carry out your responsibilities for you. If he did, He would not have allowed His only Son Jesus to come and die for our sins. It was a battle Jesus needed to fight for himself and when He did, He was elevated, He was glorified and now He is seated in the heavenly places, precisely at the right hand of God the Father and He is reigning with Him in glory. Hmmm! Long letter, isn't it?

Son, it is not yet over, that same not-easy-to-catch girl is still going to be a not-so-easy-to-marry wife. Do not get me wrong here; her personality invariably has not changed but her status has by virtue of your union, while living with her as a wife, you are going to have to keep fighting. You must continue to persevere in all things. God persisted in bringing us to Himself; He did not compel us and He is still doing so in many areas of our lives. I persisted in keeping my faith throughout all the troubles you gave me. I did not push you away or disown you, so now it is your turn to persist with someone else. A virtuous wife, who can find? Patience is the keyword if you want to find one but remember that you don't find a missing treasure in a hurry, you do take your time. The result of taking your time would be having a perfect wife that you had always dreamt about. I get mad at people when they ask God for a perfect wife. Asking God for that is like asking the doctor to hand over to a woman a grown baby at birth. I am very sure everyone in the maternity ward would take to their heels at the sight of such a birth. The reason is that babies were expected to be babies at birth, developing gradually and reaching their individual milestones later on. God has a pattern of doing things and when we understand that, we can appreciate it.

Can I confide in you, Son? Do you know that after all these years, your dad still does not see me as anything close to a perfect wife, no matter how good people see and speak about me. But the good thing is that he has perfected in his understanding of me and knows how to deal with my issues. He does not honk the horn for me outside the house to hurry me up for an outing; he also does not try to wake me up very early in the mornings. Everyone has a weakness and do need encouragement and understanding. Your dad cannot be awake to go through the nine o'clock news headlines as he starts sleeping soon after dinner, because of his busy schedules during the day. On my own path, I am an owl; I get very active at night but too tired to wake up in the mornings; *early to bed, early to rise,* as they say. Get my point – I get up early but not as early as he would. We used to have rows over these issues but thankfully we both understand each other better now. We have both learnt obedience from what we have suffered and we are both still learning. We make adjustments to accommodate each other – I try to be on time, he tries to be awake to at least tell me how his day went, share a late evening cup of tea and watch some of our favourite preachers on the God channel with me. That summarises the scriptural principle that you can only teach someone obedience when yours is complete. The outcome is usually very positive.

I am very happy that things are working out fine for you. Look at you now, you are about to get married. At your age, you are halfway into finishing paying for your mortgage; you have a well paying job, a holiday home and all. If anyone had told you that all these would happen to you a few years back, would you have believed? I remember the year you graduated from the university and got your first job, it was everything you had ever dreamt of. All of a sudden, it seemed like your world crumbled; the entire dreams you had, your aspirations and the time you invested in that company was gone as the company went bankrupt. You wanted to go the way the job went and your entire life was about to stop. Thankfully, your dad and I prayerfully intervened. One thing your dad said to you, I could remember very well was that the devil can take your job but he cannot take the gift that God has given to you. I am very sure among other things that you heard during that period, that single word of wisdom stood out for you. Not only did it stand out for you, it opened your eyes to see that *He that is in you is greater than he that is in the world.* You saw that He was not just standing there with you, but you saw that He had endowed you with so much potential. Thankfully, He gave you strength and the ability to tap into what He had given to you for that season. You got up, brushed the dust off your shoulders and continued. As I am writing this letter, I am still thinking and asking; could it be God? Could He have orchestrated all that happened? Was He trying to bring you up to the level you are at now? Was He trying to build your faith and character? I remember that when you lost that job, you also lost everything you worked hard to build in another man's business. You were diligent, committed and productive. You tried all that you could to save that company from going down; eventually when it did, you could not bear the loss. Because of the cost and the fact that so many people would live without any source of income for a while worried you even more. Although it was another man's business, yet you came home and cried on my shoulders as you could not bear the loss. You cried as hard as you cried some time ago in your junior infant years. Years ago when you lost your most precious pencil case, you cried so much over it. It was difficult to console you but I told you that everything would be alright. I didn't know if you believed me. You looked up and asked:

'Mum, are you going to get it back, or are you going to buy another one?'

I was tempted to tell you that I was going to get it back but what if I was not able to do so; what if another child had taken it? If I decide to buy it, what if I did not find that particular one in the shop? You loved it so much, I knew. It was your favourite pencil case that came with the Power Rangers lunch box and school bag. I was careful to acknowledge that and I was careful to give you an answer. All I could do was to sit you on my knee, bent your head over my shoulder and you rested and slept for a long while. You were a child then and that's how God sees us when we lose our precious things, the things we treasure or place value on. You treasured that job so much and when you lost it, I could still hear you ask;
'Is God going to replace it with a new one or is any miracle going to happen so that the old one could be revived?'

Just like your mum, God wants you to relax on His shoulder, rest and if possible, sleep. This is because while you are obediently resting on His shoulder, He does not sleep nor slumber. He is constantly working in the background for you, thinking out the best solution to your crisis. He is in the mess with you and I sincerely think that he will not like to hang around in a mess; just obey. He will handle the situation better than your mum would. It was when you moved back home for a short period that I could hear you get up at night to pray. You have always loved food but I noticed that you avoided it and read your Bible a whole lot more. That was when I began to reckon that your relationship with God had become stronger. God likes to build your character when the enemy would make an attempt on your gifts; your gifts could be your life, your marriage, your family or something very dear to you. Remember, it is not the time to cry, complain or start calling on friends. It is a time to invite God and to ask Him for strength and wisdom to do that which is extraordinary; a time to pray more and study the word of God. I know from experiences gathered in the past that our afflictions, if we remain in faith,

would be for a little while. Weeping *endureth* for a night but joy comes in the morning.
Look at you now!

God has restored all that the cankerworms and caterpillars had eaten from you and in fact you have more now than then. Truly, he is the God of restoration. No wonder the Bible says that when the devil comes to you like a flood, the Lord will raise a standard against him. The devil came as a flood but the Lord fought and conquered him. The standard of God's character in you was too hot for the enemy to handle. I tell you what, when he cools his head, he will be back to try you again. He has no peace as he moves about like a roaring lion, seeking whom he may devour. You should not be unaware of this knowing fully well that the battle has already been won in your favour. Always remember, *it's not yet over until it's over.* Always be ready to raise a higher bar and do not relent. During such times of trilas, study the scriptures; fellowship with the saints and stay in

God's presence. At the end, still come home and act in line with your beliefs, loving and cherishing your wife. You may prepare mouth-watering dinner for her. Don't ask me how as I had already taught you how to prepare some meals. I had to teach you to cook because I knew that someday, it would be useful as I would no longer be there to cook for you. My cooking then was not your favourite though, whenever you came back from school, instead of

'Hello mum' and

'How was your day',

You stood by the door and asked

'Mum, what's for lunch?'

If I made something you didn't like, all that I heard was, Yuck! or 'Oh mum, this is disgusting!' The last straw that broke the camel's back was the day you exclaimed,

'Oh mum! Is that for the garbage again?'

I got really mad Son and I thought, oh well, it's about time you learnt to prepare something for the garbage.

I thought you had really gone beyond your boundaries and I was really mad. So I decided that you must learn. I started with boiling eggs using the egg cooker and making a simple omelette. We learnt how to prepare a proper English breakfast although we never had time to eat that except on weekends. Your brother hated mushrooms but the rest of us didn't. We all ate fried or grilled sausages, baked beans, poached or lightly fried eggs, tomatoes and bacon. Don't forget your wholemeal bread; you could eat white bread if that is what she likes, a glass or even a half glass of freshly squeezed orange would be fine as the fresh smell of it would awaken anyone. Just take your time to find out; she may be like your mum who loves her porridge and yogurt every morning. We learned how to boil rice and pasta and how to prepare their sauces. It was fun for you and you wanted to learn more and more. I remember the first time you heard me use that phrase *herb of Provence;* you wondered what it was as it sounded like a mystery to you. I remember having explained to you that it was made of just six herbs – thyme, marjoram, oregano, parsley, sage and basil. It is excellent for seasoning all sorts of meat before cooking. Once the meat was well seasoned, you can roast or cook it and relax to a good meal. You loved cinnamon; the smell of spices builds your appetite. I taught you how to make simple apple cake, which can do for a good dessert. Dessert can also be bought. Yes it is inconsequential whether you bought it or made it. Actually you are allowed to cheat on this issue – you can buy ice cream in the flavour of your choice, cakes, trifle or even biscuits. Fish meals are very delicious and healthy. I know some people don't like fish that much but you can try making something from the recipe I gave you. You can do salmon steak, which you see us eat a lot; add anything you like to it, including salt, pepper and lemon. You can roast it with potatoes or even eat it with vegetables alone. Vegetables such as broccoli and carrots used to be our favourites; they taste very nice and they are easy to make.

You can serve it with red wine or any wine of your choice. Before you serve that lovely food, clean up the mess from your cooking. There is no call for abandoning the kitchen and pretending or forgetting that some cleaning has to be done in it. Cleaning up completes the cooking exercise and would bring a smile to your wife's face. Clean worktops, clean the floor, and do the dishes after everything.

I am particularly not very proud about one thing Son, you know what it is; I taught you to clean up more when we are expecting visitors or should I say I did not teach you that but I gave you that impression. I truly learnt that from my mother but I want you to break that habit. I remember in those days, the moment you saw me cleaning like never before, you would quickly ask,

'Mum, are we expecting visitors?'

Funny, but that was true. The house is for living, so clean it at all times, knowing that God is holy and cleanliness is an aspect of God's holiness -

Mum's theology! Yes, we are still on cleaning. You used to sweat a lot whenever you were asked to do something in the kitchen. Could it be that your body system couldn't stand the heat or what? We all used to tease you a lot then. Anyway, I don't know what has changed now. It's important that you take a shower after cooking Son, don't leave it for another time as a quick one will do, especially if you are making a surprise dinner for her and she is yet to get back. Put on nice cologne and a fresh top. Set an atmosphere for love and romance; create a room that is suggestive of something which you two can figure out later. Put on soft music in the background, have your sweet smelling candles lit before she gets back and a fire burning if need be. Don't forget your flowers and drinks. All these preparations should be made in advance and remember, you don't have to do all these because I know how busy you can get with your job. This detailed treatment is something you should look forward to and at such times Son, you should turn your phone off and switch off to the rest of the world. Intimate moments do not require distractions; little wonder God visited Adam and Eve in the cool of the day and that means when businesses have closed and everyone was minding their own business. He needed their undivided attention and a high level of concentration from them. Such special times are worth the time and effort.

Have you ever wondered why your dad and I would let your Auntie take care of you sometimes, even when we both had nowhere to go? In a quiet mood, two of you will open up to each other, your pride and shame would be gone and the real you will show up. You will begin to hear each other's heartbeat. Welcome her back with kisses, with loving words and a seductive bubble bath with a scented bar of soap, if she likes one. I am sure every woman would love one from a husband after a hard day's work. Ensure that you have her fluffy towel and robe at hand. You two need extreme peace and quiet with soft music and mood light in your bedroom. Note Son, this can only happen when the time comes, when you are permitted to have her to yourself as your lawful wedded wife. Then you two can lie together in the quietness of that softly lit room, full of the aroma of essential oils, which could be cinnamon that you like, lavender, vanilla or even jasmine and a soft sensual music to suit the mood. You can lie close to each other, feeling one another's heartbeat without shame or regrets. No regrets Son, rather you will want to cover her whole face and body with the kisses of your lips as you want her to know how much you love and cherish her. Envelop her in your arms and reassure her that with you she will forever be cherished and protected. Always remember to wait for her to be ready and don't ever be in a hurry. Take it to the bank; I am sure she will be ready after such attention. Trust your mother, she will be ready. Always remember, it must not be in the bedroom, so do not create a limit. Wherever you are standing is a holy ground. God can meet you anywhere you want to meet Him. All he needs is your undivided attention and solitude. It does not take much to have intimacy if you want to. Susanna Wesley, in the midst of her bunch of children always had her quiet time. The moment her apron covers her face, her intimacy with God began.

Don't forget the bin; always remember that you are obliged to take the rubbish outside for the bin man to collect. I am not going to be there to remind you, so it's important you devise a means whereby you can remember the collection dates. If your wife does it, then it will be very considerate and good of her but if she doesn't, don't hold it against her. The responsibility of running the house is on both of you anyway and you should see it as such. Always remember that she is not your brother who would usually take turns with you in helping out with chores. Just sitting here writing this letter, I can still see your rotas – the rota for doing the dishes, the rota for taking the rubbish out, the rota for ironing; there is a rota for everything. The only rota you did not have ready was a rota for cleaning the toilet seat. I often went to inspect the toilet after you had used it and if you had left it messed up, would demand that you get back to clean it up. It's not going to be so in this relationship as there will not be room for arguing over whose turn it is today and whose it was yesterday. She is only a perfect helpmeet for you, so get up and exercise those muscles.

I was reliably informed by your brother that you are now cutting down on your food intake just to shed some weight for the wedding. I also gathered that you are regular at the gym located very close to your office. This is interesting but be aware that you don't have to overdo things and push yourself too hard. Set realistic goals and walk towards achieving them. Small steps and small changes are good and don't forget that a little goes a long way and has lasting effects. Try and eat normal portions of proper balanced diet as you are exactly what you eat. Growing up, a friend of mine visited me one day and when she opened my cupboard, she said *weird*! She saw the kind of things I loved to eat, things like brown pasta, brown rice, nuts, oats and brown bread. She said *'you sure do eat like a bird, and you will fly one day.'* I was delighted at her comment because I really wanted to be able to fly some day. If you eat more carbohydrates and fats you will grow fat and overweight and won't be able to fly. But if you eat less carbohydrates, more fruit and vegetables like I had mentioned earlier in this letter, you will be just fine. Likewise with the Word of God; if you keep feeding on the Word of God, you will soon become what you feed on. Your life will be lighter and you will have more joy, more peace, more love, more hope and you will build your most holy faith. But if you don't and keep feeding on other things that are not profitable, they will definitely yield negative results. Fear, anxiety, sickness, depression and death are the results of engaging in things that are not profitable. Regular exercise is good and you cannot over emphasize on the importance of physical fitness. You need to be fit to think properly, work with dedication, play and to demonstrate that you love your spouse effectively. However, remember to do everything in moderation. The six pack abs and *Hulk Hogan* physique cannot come overnight if you have not started building it long before now. You may get hurt if you attempt to do so much within such a short time. As a matter of fact, the Bible says that physical exercise profits little but spiritual exercise profits much. If you want to lose real weight, go to God in prayer and fasting. When you have kicked out those habits that you cannot do without, by the strength that is in the power of Jesus, they will all be replaced with a healthy lifestyle. God will give you the ability and motivation to sustain your new lifestyle and then you can hit the gym. Moreover, if you want to exercise and keep fit for the sake of the wedding, it will be for the wedding, but if you get active as part of a continuous healthy regime, then it will be all yours for keeps.

The ability and motivation to do unusual things can only come from God. In this regard, I am wondering whether to tell you something that I have been thinking about lately. Be patient with me as I will not be long on this matter. You know that God has blessed you richly and endowed you with wisdom. You have everything going for you in your workplace and money is not much of a problem. You are the number three man in the whole company and you are happy with that. You travel as much as you want to with all expenses paid for by the company, and you always looked forward to that. So tell me, why do you sound frustrated when you talk about your job, this perfect job that has given you back everything? Why do you sigh whenever you begin a story about this wonderful job you have? For me Son, whenever I am frustrated or not completely happy with a situation, it meant that I needed a change. Yes, I needed to change the situation or change my position. In your case, I don't think you have what it takes to change the situation; you cannot, even if you try. Son, you definitely have what it takes to change your position. I think now is the time to start something you can call your own; your own company. Yes, because I feel that working for others has not allowed you to give your gifts and talents the fullest expression they crave. When you work for people, they remain your bosses; you hang your hopes on them; you have limited capacity and only dance according to the tunes they play. Remember the saying that, *He who pays the piper dictates the tunes*. You cannot reach your full potential because you are limited by certain rules and regulations which apply only to people who are employed. You are limited by the terms and conditions that apply to your employment contract which you may not have interpreted well from the start; it only favours those that wrote it. That is exactly why you are frustrated. But when you work for yourself, you have the freedom to think about the future; freedom to focus and even get involved in other things as you are led. You would no longer be restricted by another man's terms and conditions and in fact the only restrictions and limitations you have would be *yourself.* You would have full expression and make your own decisions.

If you take this step, you would become your own driver and could drive yourself to wherever you want. You could drive yourself to your destiny. Think about it Son, you will create employment for people in the house of God which will give them the dignity to provide for themselves and you will no longer give money to them for food, only for them to come the next time asking for more. I am not saying that giving is a bad thing, after all *God loves a cheerful giver* and if you give, it shall be given back to you. However I want you to remember the popular saying, *'don't just give people fish; instead, teach them how to catch one'*. You will be helping some people stand on their feet if you start something you can call your own today. Bishop Tudor Bismark from Zimbabwe is a minister I love so much. In one of his topics, he said that he does not only want to be taught how to fish, but he wants to own his own fishing pond. His reason was that if he only knew how to fish, the owner of the fishing pond may come one day and then he will not be allowed to fish in it. You will employ people and also manifest your gifts, abilities and talents as a child of God. That is what the earnest expectations of God's creation are waiting for. You will empower people and in so doing, the kingdom of God will keep expanding. The kingdom of God is not only in words but it is also in action – will you let God use you? Move to a higher level Son, a higher level. I am not unaware of the indescribable gifts and abilities that God has given to you Son. I also know that He can increase your capacity to manifest these gifts. Many preachers and talk show hosts would say these days: *'you have God's DNA in you'*. His creative and *'can do'* abilities reside in you, so it's up to you to tap into those inherent abilities and to begin to do extra-ordinary things with them. Like Mary the mother of Jesus, I am persuading you to use your talents so that the wine will be more than enough and even sweeter for the people in the house of God. The issue I have been trying to raise here is called entrepreneurship. You are quite familiar with this phrase because you are a smart, creative, wise and intelligent young man.

You are an epitome of God's strength and wisdom; you have the power to create wealth and ability to multiply. You can do all things through Christ who gives you strength. The key phrase here is '*all things*'. Entrepreneurship and small businesses are the driving force behind many economies of today. Bigger organisations and institutions like the one you work for are failing and can no longer be relied upon. Yes, they are all failing and turning people's lives upside down, like they were going to do to you earlier when you first started. Get me right, it's not necessarily about the money; you may not be able to make as much as you are doing now initially but with time you will definitely reap the fruit of your labour.

Don't let them hold you back Son.

I remember the model Titanic ship you built when you were only nine years old. You took it to school to show off and your teacher asked you to take it to all the classes and do *'show and tell'*, as you called it. According to you my Son, one of your friends *David,* said that his dad was a builder and could build a shop for both of you so that you could start a company where he would be selling, while you make more ships. What an excellent idea from a child as young as you were then. The concept that the child was bringing then is called networking. As a well-informed person, I am sure by now that you must be used to that word. Networking is a very good method businessmen and women use these days to start and to grow their businesses. Just like that boy suggested, you can get people to do some aspects of your job and you can still make your profits. The good thing is that you can take some unnecessary costs, overheads and headaches off your table. Please don't misunderstand me and don't also think that I am asking for too much from God on your behalf. Well I guess that God is not complaining as His source of supply is inexhaustible. Remember that I owe you a duty to tell you the truth and I cannot deceive you. You also know quite well that it is not in my character to add to anyone's stress or push them beyond their capacities, let alone my dearest Son.

Your dad, whenever he was asked what his favourite animal in the Bible is, quickly says *'the ant'* and I often wondered why the ant? Then one day, I saw that the ant is a very wise insect that gathers its food in a particular season when it is favourable to do so, knowing that another season is coming when he is not able to gather anymore. Then he sits down and eat the food he has gathered in the previous season. Be like the ant Son, this is your season and your time; make use of the opportunities you have while you can. Don't settle for anything less. Do you remember your dad's friend who used to be an estate developer? Sometime in the past, he got for himself a huge job with the government to develop a housing estate. You cannot believe the amount of jobs he created for the people in the local Church. He employed architects, engineers, plumbers, painters, minor job labourers and in fact my friend who was looking for a job got a contract to supply lunch to all the site workers. What a blessing it was to the house of God as he continues to develop estates, one after the other! If you ever decide to give it a go, as I am sure you soon will and also because I know whose Son you are, do not have any sense of guilt. Do not feel guilty that you are pulling out but make sure that you don't tamper with their ideas or resources. I know that you won't.

By the way, most people who are in their own businesses started the same way although some may have been fired or made redundant, which wouldn't be your case. Guilt is the first thing which the devil would want to bring to your mind. He hates it a lot when we make progress or want to move on to the next level. He will bring doubt, fear and unbelief. He likes intimidation, but do not give room to his antics. Remember, the righteous is as bold as a lion. You have to be bold and strong for the Lord your God is with you and He will bless the works of your hands. Just know that you are taking the right steps whenever you want to move. However, you have to be as wise as a serpent and as harmless as a dove. The people, who had employed you all these years, know your potentials and they won't let you go without a fight. Remember the story of Jacob and his father-in-law. The Bible records that when Jacob decided to leave Laban his master after several years of serving him, Laban became disagreeable because he understood that Jacob had a huge potential and that God's favour was upon him. He could not take it easily and devised tricks and all manner of gimmicks just to intimidate Jacob. In all, God still favoured Jacob and set him free because he was faithful and upright. He never defrauded his master at any point in time.

So be not ignorant of the devices of the enemy, Son. Keep watch at this time because at the end, just like Jacob, God will set you free. You have served like Jacob and if you apply faith like his father Abraham, God will prosper the works of your hands and will bring you to that land of promise.

Experience they say, is the best teacher. However, you don't have to go through every negative experience in life to learn. Think about it, if researchers had carried out certain laborious experiments and came out with conclusive results, you don't need to start experimenting on those anymore, because they have been tested and proven to be right. You know that I worked in the community crèche for many years in my younger years, where children are allowed to play trial and error. In fact, some activities are planned for them to try things out and make mistakes. That is when you would see them trying to fit a circular cup into a triangular hole which is very funny to watch! It really used to be hilarious working with the kids. You are no longer a child, so I want you to learn from my own experiences and to also learn from the vast array of experiences of other people. My point is that I worked for people for far too long and as a result, I didn't know when to call it quits. I wasted my energy for other people's benefit, most of the times feeling frustrated, dejected and used. Otherwise, if I had put that energy into my own private business doing the same job, it would have been a different experience. I may not have retired, and there would still have been some kind of profession, income and satisfaction coming from the venture. Your dad was wiser as he pushed his creativity to the maximum; he never worked for anyone. He enjoyed his freedom and had lots of time for you guys. I don't regret my life at all but why should I? You could remember how I sought for my first proper job like I did search for a job forever. At that time, it seemed as if everyone around me had a well paying job as all my friends worked and earned their own money. I was the only one left out. I cried daily because I needed to go out and meet with people. I needed to buy some designer shoes and handbags; I needed to hold workplace conversations when my friends were around just as they would talk about theirs. Families were getting expensive things in their homes; replacing the old ones at will; going on expensive holidays and to add to it, you always asked for toys and such things which we considered luxury. Unfortunately I could not do so much as we were managing on one income. Although your dad never complained, we lived on a shoestring budget. I prayed all manner of prayers to God, asking him to improve our situation by providing me with something that would give us additional income. God did answer that prayer when I prayed correctly. All I did was to stop asking for selfish reasons. I remember one night having prayed, I heard God ask me to present a good reason why I wanted a job. I was afraid to give an answer because I wanted to answer correctly as I knew it was God speaking to me. It's not that often that you hear God that clearly and I wanted to give Him a precise and correct answer like Solomon did when he had that chance and he asked for wisdom. I didn't want to blow that chance. I have come to realise the pattern He uses in dealing with me and with the people He loves. So that night as I went to bed, I dreamed that God created Eve from Adam's rib to be a helpmeet for Adam. I woke up in the morning more confused. However before the end of that day, everything came together. I realised that I was created to use all that I am and all that I have to help your dad and everyone around me. Your dad needed to work less so that he could have more time with his children. Son, at that particular moment, I went on my knees to God to make my argument and to simply plead my case with Him. I told God that I have realised that I need to earn money and I asked God to bless me with material resources. I gave Him all my reasons and it was approved in the court of Heaven. God does not answer prayers – scandalous? Yes, He looks at the motives behind your requests most times. So that was one of my testimonies and I don't and will never forget God's goodness concerning how I went into that job.

So now that I have finished with employment and have retired as you already know, I am not lonely and complaining. I don't sit around as in those days expecting people to visit me or call me on the phone and when they don't, I start wondering why. I also don't sit around anymore watching television all day long. I suddenly discovered that when you are gainfully employed, the twenty four hours of the day run rather quickly. But how can I be lonely? Was it not Dr. Cindy Trim, the renowned African-American motivational speaker and preacher of *The Word*, who said that *loneliness is not the absence of people but the absence of purpose.* God has rewarded me with a great purpose, a great mission, a mission which I must accomplish. I hardly have time these days because I have gone full-time into the pet project I left years back. It is a project that caters for young girls in many rural regions of Africa. I called it *Padz for Pals*. If you could recall, I used to go about collecting sanitary pads, with the help of the Stevens. They gave me lots of encouragement and support then as according to them, it was a worthy course. I went about collecting sanitary pads to be sent to girls in rural Africa and other less privileged countries, distributing them to schools and Churches. You and your brother used to call those pads *'mums diapers'*.

You could not get your head around with what they were used for then, but I knew you definitely would know when the time is right, so I did not bother my head explaining to you. That time is now. I am sure you saw lots of them in your biology and science classes. But the bit I would really love you to know is that your wife-to-be will also have pads in her possession. You will see it a lot during her menstruation every month. You don't have to feel indifferent about it. I understand this as a time when you may feel uncomfortable having an intimate relationship with her. Try to find out how she feels about it and remember to always be patient with her. Ensure at this time that you let her know that she is very attractive and beautiful and make her comfortable. Some women get some cramps; some may feel very sick, while others don't even feel any thing. It used to be a very difficult time for my sister. Growing up, she missed one of her important exams as a result of her menstrual period. It used to be dreadful and we never looked forward to that time of the month in the family. Buy her gifts and take her out especially if she does not want a certain level of intimacy with you for any reason. But to be truthful to you, there is no reason why both of you cannot enjoy intimacy at all times. Don't go asking Google, because I know you will do that. It's quite healthy for both of you; healthier than your head could imagine. Research has proven that intimate relationship at this time will help her to shorten the menstrual period. However, the decision to have intimacy at this time is completely a personal choice that both of you have to make.

So I am back on my feet with the *Padz for Pals* project. I could not continue with that vision because of lack of funds and I could not co-ordinate it properly then. The few people, to whom I mentioned it then, did not catch the vision and did not see the need for me to go and stand in front of supermarkets, schools and shops collecting sanitary pads for girls. I was also not very confident in my abilities and convictions at that time and I did not have all the information that I have now. At one time I was asked to explain what the whole project was all about but because I did not have it written down, I simply could not. I know better now and can confidently defend the cause. Another reason why we could not go ahead with the project was because I had only your dad when you were growing up and we had no help from any extended family member. This was in addition to the fact that I had to put in a few hours at work to help dad with the bills. I also needed to interact with the outside world just to maintain my sanity. But I always knew that every vision is for an appointed time. I knew it was never going to die because whatever that is born of God overcomes and does not die. So I have started it all over again and it is humbling and at the same time a pleasure to know that God had called me and gone further to choose me as one of the vessels to use to extend the work of His kingdom in this end time. You will ask me why pads? Why can they not buy ordinary pads? You see, it is easy to take for granted a thing as common as a sanitary pad for some girls in these communities but the fact remains that it is a luxury for most girls who are lucky to receive them from us. Without ours, they use rags during menstruation. Society discriminates against poor people because of the margin that poverty creates. In any given society, there are the '*haves*' and the *have-nots*. Even the Bible says that *you will always have the poor among you.* You need not look far to see this gap between the '*haves*' and the *have-nots* who are left to struggle on their own without any kind of welfare or support system. But Son, you need to see these people's level of resilience, the adults and children alike. In the face of these difficulties, most of them still find reasons to smile and to move on; they are actually some of the happiest people I have met in my entire life. This is the opposite of what you see with people who have abundance. For some people, although they have everything, a little problem gives rise to depression, anxiety, fear, or suicidal thoughts and it really amazes me. In the developing society, the '*have-nots*' tend to serve the '*haves*'. They are used as slaves and housemaids and sometimes perceived as scoundrels, evil, criminals, liars and carriers of deadly diseases. The effect is that most of them have resigned to fate, which leaves them in abject poverty as they cannot afford the basic necessities of life. They get poorer and poorer and wait for the day help will come from some *good Samaritans*. Others, who do not have the boldness to engage in criminal activities to earn a living, may subsequently die of hunger.

The sad thing about these people is that society looks at their story from a single side as Ngozi Chimamanda Adichie strongly worded it in one of her presentations in a *'Ted talk'* show. *'Ted talk'*, as I am sure you remember, is one of those Internet talk shows that I was and still am obsessed with. A single-sided story, as my friend Ngozi puts it, has a huge disadvantage. People have been labelled prostitutes, criminals, and housemaids, resulting in their story being boxed away. No one wants to know the other side of them which may have some rays of light. They could have some untapped potentials, which if properly harnessed, could benefit them as well as society. Some of them have ambitions, talents, dreams, visions and gifts which are still locked up inside them. Unfortunately, people who are very close to them do not usually see that side of them. They only see the good in them as long as they serve them. They need people at their beck and call, people who will answer them *'Sir'* and *'Ma'*. They need them as cooks, gate men, gardeners and cleaners. Some of them have been raped, abused and written off, not surprisingly though by their so-called masters. Son, get me right here. In life, all fingers are not equal and if I may say it as the writer of *'Animal Farm'* mildly put it: *'All animals are equal; some are just more equal than others'*. This is a true quote all over the world. In the Bible, Boaz had gleaners in his field. Inequality is a global phenomenon. If people are not saying it, they behave it. Think about the inequality in gender, in employment, in disability and in race just to mention but a few. These are all crimes against humanity and should be fought from every angle and at every level.

For the purpose of this letter to you, I am only allowed by my instinct to talk about domestic helps in developing countries and how they are abused. I am aware that some people would argue the fact that these house-helps are not treated as bad as people like us often portray them to the rest of the world. I really do not know about that claim, rather I know that evil should be called evil. Moreover, if the house-helps are being done a favour, why don't some of their master's kids go and get such good favours? No, rather they are sent to the best schools abroad. While studying, they live in the best houses, drive the best cars and most of these kids become problems to the society in which they find themselves in and a total disgrace to their parents and home country. I am not judging, condemning or even pointing accusing fingers, rather my aim is and indeed everyone's aims should be to persuade people, communities and governments to change their thoughts and attitudes towards inequality and crimes against humanity. That is what the word of God does; it does not condemn people – rather it changes people's ways of thinking and behaviours. When this happens, you would hear people using the phrase *'I am born again'*.

I would have been one of those people who think that getting house-helps is a way of helping their families at home or giving them a livelihood if I had not had an encounter with some of them. One of the girls we picked up on the street one night was repeatedly raped at night by this man she called *master*. She eventually got pregnant and when the *master's* wife discovered what had happened, she sent her packing in the middle of the night with no money and no place to go. She briefly told us that when her master made advances at her, she tried fighting her way out of it but he threatened to throw her out of the house if she refused to cooperate with him. She was afraid of being thrown out into what seemed to be the oblivion where she came from. On that cold night when we met her, it rained heavily with lightning and thunder thriving in turns. Normally when it rains in that part of the world, the electric power is disrupted and there would be thick darkness all over. I am sure you must be wondering by now what in the name of '*outreach*' we were doing in such weather conditions. Yes Son, none of us had anticipated that level of rain that night and of course there was no weather forecast in the news. We had all gone out to work earlier in the day and it was on our way back that the rain caught up with us. Thank God for the lightning in the midst of the rain. We wouldn't have seen this girl in that thick darkness had it not been for the flashes of light. As the lightening flashed, she cast a dark shadow on our path, which gave us the incline that there might be someone there. So we went back and there she was.

Sometimes as you drive, you would see someone with mental illness lying at the corner of the street or walking about aimlessly. They would not have any blanket and some of the women would have menstrual stains on their clothes with flies following them. Unfortunately no one cared about them as they ate from the bin and never took a bath. Only the rain that fell on them from time to time became their bath. They were simply left to die. When we asked the reason why, we were told that some of them were mad because of the evils committed by their parents in the past and that the gods were punishing them as a result. For a moment I would stand still to ponder on the nature of the God we serve, who is full of mercies and compassion, who said *I will be merciful unto their unrighteousness and their sins I will remember no more.* Of a truth, the Christian God is different. Another group of ladies told us that they have been used for rituals. You hear such stories and wonder what could have been said about hundreds of people who live in comfortable care residences, the mental and rehabilitation homes in the western world; what could have been said about them or even their families if they were to be in this society? You think of women who have post-natal depression as a result of different factors and all the support they receive from everyone, as against one of the women we met, who, it was alleged, had an evil spirit that tormented her every time she gave birth. We were not trained to provide intervention and support for such people rather than the simple practical assistance that we had, which brought us there in the first place. In some unfortunate cases, they threw our gifts back at us because of the suspicion arising from their lack of knowledge. They did not understand the reason for our kind gestures. Nevertheless, it was usually painful to see people in this inhuman condition and not do anything.

So this girl shivering with cold at that ungodly hour was asked who she was and what she was doing out at that time of the night, and she told us that her name was *Ada*. According to her, all that she could remember as a child about her mum was that she had gone overseas by boat. Then as often as she asked about her mum who apparently had her as a single mother, they told her that she would come home one day.

As she spoke, my mind went back to thousands of Africans who had in the time past drowned at sea, while emigrating to Europe looking for greener pastures and never made it to their destinations. I tried to have faith that someday this girl's mum would come home and be reunited with her daughter.

A second girl recounted her ordeal, how she was labelled a witch because a child in her care who had malaria screamed her name during one of her nightmares. She was beaten and disgraced by the family she was serving and then sent away. I wondered what other names these children could have called in such circumstances, when the only parents they practically knew were their carers. I wondered who I would call or run to in times of trouble as a Christian, if not God who sees to my daily needs. It is so simple to understand; it is not rocket science, except that people shut their minds out to this common sense and reasoning. When we picked up this second girl, she told us that she had no family and that the only person she could have gone to was her grandmother. Sadly, her grandmother had passed away months back as the villagers stoned her to death, because they also claimed that she was a witch. *'Sister'*, she called out. She referred to all of us as *Sister* because we had a *Nun* in our company. Looking up from the floor where she sat, she looked directly into my eyes as though I was the only person who would believe her sincerity and prove her grandmother innocent though dead. She narrated her story to us; my grandmother was a good person and very good to me', she told us. 'After the death of my parents, she started caring for me with the little she had until my master came to tell her that they would send me to school. It was a relief when they came, although I was a bit hesitant. I wanted to stay back with her as she was all that I had. If I had known that they were not going to fulfill their promise of sending me to school, I wouldn't have left grandma by herself. She suffered greatly in her sickness because no one could bring her to a hospital. She got so sick and started forgetting things; in the evening she would wander about inside the village and children made fun of her. My master's dad forgets things too; sometimes he urinates and passes stools on himself. When my master heard of his father's condition in the village, he quickly went down to the village and brought him to the city. He hired a doctor who comes to see him every other day. His medication alone filled one cupboard. No one called him a witch when he started talking about his friends that died years ago as though they were playing '*Okwe*' (a local board game). No one called him a witch when he engaged in conversations at the middle of the day with one of his late wives. When Grandma was very ill, I did not hear about it. No one informed me about her condition and it was kept away from me. I would have gone home to take care of her. I know she was never a witch.

She concluded her story.

She was not a witch; we comforted her in the midst of her sobs. Of course these men and women after sending their victims away will proceed to look for another. All that such girls needed was for someone to give them a little hope, encourage them, tell them that they can pick up the pieces of their lives and move on. Someone to tell them that they can do it if they think it. Like *Mo,* a talk show host puts it, 'they need a voice like that of the United States President Obama from a higher platform telling them *'yes you can'*.

So Son, that is my current passion as it has always been but I have just decided to reignite it to serve humanity. I never saw Mother Teresa, I may not in my lifetime be able to meet Oprah Winfrey, though that would be a privilege, I may not be able to see all the good people I had mentioned in this book but I want to live and see the world they lived in and I want to walk the path they walked;

a world that gives people hope and shows them compassion. That is what your mother wants now and it is this purpose that wakes me up every morning and gives me the drive throughout the day. Son, I have also learnt so much from these people I work for. The last time I was there, one of the girls was asking how she could help because she was greatly moved by our level of commitment and care. Thinking of this girl, my mind went back to the widows that we read about in the Bible. You remember the poor widow who gave all that she had to God? I applauded that girl's courage and simply told her that it is in giving that people receive. The Bible also tells us that it is better to give than to receive. She did not need to give all she had like the widow and she does not need to wait till she has much to give. I made her to understand that she could help with her talents; she could give her time by volunteering in schools and Churches. Think about it, this part of the world we live in was built on volunteering. People give all they have to see that society moves on. Sometimes when I drive out at night, I see men and women wearing high visibility jackets with *'tidy town'* written on them. These men and women move around the streets, mostly in the evenings to pick up rubbish from the streets and sometimes plant flowers. They are not paid yet they do it, not for the good of their health but they do it for the good of humanity and for posterity. *Phil* our neighbour occasionally does this cleaning in our estate by organising other residents. They do not necessarily wait for the *Tidy Town*. Because of such contributions, the community, the state and the country is a better place for everyone. The government cannot do everything for you.

What about you, Son? I need not remind you that you have to give something back to your society; remember, to whom much is given, much is expected. Take action that will enhance the quality of people's lives. God has blessed you so much that He wants to make you His channel of blessing. I remember you mentioned something like teaching the underprivileged how to use the computer – did you do that? Or are you still planning to do so? Your brother came back from Africa and told of how people were dying of malaria. I said to him that it is not really malaria that killed them; it is the mosquitoes. Think about it, if people are well informed, they will look after their environments; they will clean their gutters and try to improve on their living standards especially where it concerns cleanliness. Remember the saying, *'cleanliness is next to godliness'* and if your standard of cleanliness is not up to scratch, how then can you come near to God. The truth is that people need to be educated and there has to be awareness created by everyone who has this understanding. It is not the duty of the government – that is, if those in the government have any awareness themselves and are willing to do anything for the people they govern. The story is always that of wealth embezzlement; the wealth which was supposed to be well distributed to everyone, being taken by a privileged few who then turn around to expect the western world to send Aid to them.

So the *Pads for Pals* project functions as a social network for concerned ladies. These ladies will bring to the attention of people who should care, awareness of the monthly needs of sanitary pads for young girls in the remote areas of Africa. It is so easy to think that everyone could afford to buy a pad. But the truth remains that millions of girls cannot afford a proper pad and millions more get infections as a result of the use of rags for their *periods*. Think about the girls in war-ravaged zones or about those living where there are constant natural disasters. Some of these girls do not even know what a pad is because they have never seen one. If they have, they cannot afford it. Some girls stay away from school on such days because they cannot afford a pad. Others are asked not to come to Church because it is wrongly believed that they will defile the house of God. What a pity! But with members of *Padz for Pals* scattered across this continent, I hope the story would change. It is only a call out to the previleged to reach out to these less privileged girls. Our mission is to create an awareness of this need with the hope that individuals and governments will recognise this as part of the needs of families and children. Proper education on this matter will ultimately improve health and hygiene, reduce teenage pregnancies and death from pregnancy related complications. As the girls learn more about their body and how it works, they will understand the importance of personal hygiene and the consequences of neglect. The sanitary pads hence become the tool for teaching topics such as sexually transmitted diseases and how to say '*no*' to men who want to offer them temporary relief and take advantage of their situations. When I look at these girls, their eyes tell me that there is something that they are seeking; fortunately enough, most answers to their questions are with people like you and I. We need to teach them some survival mechanisms, how they can fend for themselves through some training that our organisation provides.

Have a look at a poem I wrote about this project from the deepest part of my heart:

Give a gift of a pad or more
Make a note on pads to say
How fun it is to be a girl
How wise to say no and win
How to use your hands and live
How to walk with shoulders high
How to pray and work for the best

Son, there are many things you can do at your leisure; ask God for wisdom and don't be slothful, like the Bible calls it, and don't *stay at ease in Zion.* The earnest creations are waiting for the manifestation of the sons of God. I pray that the good Lord will manifest His power through you to do His good and perfect will. Amen.

I would like to be remembered as a good grandma by my grandchildren someday. I will enjoy going to the mirror and seeing my hair all turned grey. Most importantly, still standing behind me, your dad, who will look into my tired eyes with kindness and still remember my bold and beautiful eyes and the first day he saw them, telling me how attractive and beautiful I still looked. Don't get me wrong now; I am not saying that you two should start making babies when you are not ready for them so that I can become a grandma, as some women demand. No, I will enjoy being a grandmother and will be willing to be a good one, whenever you two or even your brothers are ready to make me one. In this regard as in all others, always remember to seek God's face before embarking on major decisions in your life. I have never seen any decision as hard, yet important as having babies. You need to pray and be really ready to give it your all. Let the Lord know about it beforehand and He will give the journey the smooth ride it deserves. If possible, find out the reason why you want to have children. This may sound very strange; yes, you already know this story that I am about to tell you. You came nearly seven years after your dad and I were married and we desperately wanted a child. At a time I became worried that I was not going to have a baby. Our friends and family were worried, the church prayed all manner of prayers for us and yet nothing happened. I did a lot of fasting and yet I did not hear from God.

I remember that I used to have a prayer partner, a very phenomenal lady who was in a similar situation then. It was not long after we began praying together that she got pregnant and had a daughter. She gave her daughter a beautiful name *Nmesoma,* which is interpreted as the *'goodness of the Lord'*. I became more worried and queried God's goodness over my own life.

No wonder the Bible says that two women would be grinding in the mill, one would be taken and the other would be left. I felt left out and felt terrible. I became afraid that I was going to lose my friend. I wondered who I was going to share this burden with and who I was going to pray with. My *holy mind* became envious of her as a result of my narrow mindedness and faithlessness at that time. To worsen the matter my friend became very ill as soon as her pregnancy was confirmed and she was not able to meet up at our regular place of prayer. I felt terribly rejected, terribly offended and I thought that she was doing that because she has been sorted out. I thought of so many things as I was ignorant of sicknesses that go with early pregnancies. I felt that the Lord had rejected me. I went in for a lot of hospital procedures and yet the doctors could not find one single thing that was wrong with me. I remember one of the numerous prayers that I prayed then and that was for God to please give me a child, because I wanted to know what my children would look like. I prayed about that among other prayers and I remember your dad asking God to give us a child that would look and behave like us and I wondered if God was going to give us twins or a child with an image of two people. Put very simply Son, when two people marry, they become one. The Bible says that a man shall leave his mother and father, and shall cleave to his wife and the two will become one in expression. Little did we know that this prayer was our *strong reason*. Those two prayers were right and formed our strong reasons before the Lord; they were the right prayers. Just remember what the Bible says, that our prayers are not answered because we do not pray aright. It entreats that we should present our strong reasons before Him. That we did, without really knowing the full implications of what we were asking for. Then you came; you were so sweet, so angelic, a wonder to behold and a miracle I cannot forget in a hurry. Son you were a carbon copy of your dad, and you behaved exactly like us. At your birth, I sang Hannah's song, prayed and danced like she did at the birth of Samuel; for there is no one like God.

Years later, in your teenage years, you began to develop some strange attitudes. As you would imagine, people, books and common sense called your behaviour all sorts of names and then went further to tell us that it was a stage. A stage that we felt was lasting forever. They called it peer pressure, they called it hormones, genes, and others called it environmental factors or the fact that you were even a boy. I began to hear that phrase that *'Boys will be Boys'* They told us that it was normal. My father (your grandfather) said *'hapu ya'* (meaning: leave him alone). I ignored that because I thought that it was one of those elements children share with their grandparents. Although I realised later that Jesus had used that same word in the parable of the wheat and the tares. In that parable, His disciples had reported to Him that the enemy had sown tares among the wheat in the night. They were worried and desperately needed Jesus to do something. Jesus responded to them by saying '*hapu ya*' (meaning: leave it alone). At harvest time, the tares will be separated from the wheat.

All these factors according to different people contributed to the behaviour you exhibited at that stage of your life. As you would expect, they began to propose theories such as behavioural modifications. This is the treatment of human behavioural disorders through the reinforcement of acceptable behaviours and the suppression of undesirable ones. The technique has its roots in the work of *Ivan Pavlov*, a Russian physiologist who observed that animals could be taught to respond to stimuli that might otherwise have no effect on them. I tried this but could not go further because of its limitations. All these theories are good in their own way, but I discovered that they can never be as good as the application of the Word of God. I made a decision to continue to show you *love*; unconditional love like Christ showed us. Son, love has no limit; you can never go wrong in giving or even in receiving love. Love definitely withstands every trial and tribulation; love, in fact, never fails. Paul's first letter to the Corinthians chapter 13 verses 4-12 reads:

> *4. Love is patient; love is kind. It does not envy, it does not boast, it is not proud.*
>
> *5. It does not dishonour others, it is not self-seeking, it is not easily angered and it keeps no record of wrongs.*
>
> *6. Love does not delight in evil but rejoices with the truth.*
>
> *7. It always protects, always trusts, always*

hopes, and always perseveres.
8. Love never fails. But where there are prophecies, they will cease; where there are tongues, they will be stilled; where there is knowledge, it will pass away.
9. For we know in part and we prophesy in part.
10. But when completeness comes, what is in part disappears.

Yes, theories and human knowledge will disappear as they will always have limitations but love lasts forever.

Unconditional love was what I resolved to show to you but before then I spent sleepless nights crying to God, not in faith and hope but in fear and doubt; in fear of what your tomorrow would be. We were afraid that other parents would brand us incompetent. How could I have had such sleepless nights over you when I claimed to have known the Lord whom I serve? The one that says:

cast all your cares upon me, the one that says that I should not be anxious for anything but in prayer and supplication; I should make my requests known to Him. When I eventually did, his perfect love was at hand to take care of my fears and to give me hope that our tomorrow would be better than our today. Before that rest, I could not imagine how anyone would say that such behaviour was normal. As a human, I thought of ways that I had gone wrong as I searched for the origin of these behaviours. I was convinced that we never missed a Church service and you were taught in Sunday school very early in life. We had a good relationship with one another in the family. From the beginning, we neither drank nor kept late nights. I made sure that I censored what you watched on the television and I brought you up to have self-confidence and good self-image. How did you allow yourself to be influenced so much by your friends, when we did read about Daniel in the Bible so often? Daniel, according to some Bible students, was in his teenage years when he had his challenges, but could not be influenced by his peers. He could not bow to a graven image and could not even eat what others ate as it went against his beliefs. Son, Daniel simply could not afford to let himself or his God down. Attending church services and programmes became the last thing on your mind on a Sunday morning. You turned into an *á la carte* Christian who only wanted to go to church when it suited him, or on special occasions such as a christening ceremony, confirmation, wedding or Christmas Day. In fact you went to church strictly by invitation. You preferred to go to a football match or go to cinema than go to Church. The reason was that you felt that the Church was a place for the elderly and people who were dying. Your mates did their own thing on Sundays as they didn't go to Church either. However, your lack of Church attendance did not worry me too much when I realised that people like my friend Rev. Mark has dedicated their lives to reaching out to people who would not come near a Church building. Wherever they may be in the community, Rev. Mark's ministry goes – whether it's in the pub, sports club or anywhere else that you would least expect a conventional preacher to go to.

I wondered what we did wrong. Were we not insightful enough or were we too strict or cared less? Your life was simply out of sync. Should we have kept you in a bubble so that you wouldn't get to associate very well with your peers as people suggested? No, that would have been very naïve of us. As they say, if you love someone, let him go. We allowed you to have that social interaction with your peers. I looked at you sometimes then, and I wondered if I really knew who you were. Your behaviour was like that of a child from a different planet – no respect, no obedience to simple instructions and no heed to parental counsel. Surprisingly, your teachers reported that you were a good boy in class. You gave us so much trouble that we wanted to send you to somewhere far-far away, to your uncles, to anyone that would instil more discipline in you. We could not, because you are a son in our house and not a slave. I could do nothing then but to gather all those names and factors together and mention them to the Lord who said that at mention of the name of Jesus, every knee shall surely bow. If those factors have names, it meant that they have knees. I waited patiently for the day you would finally come back like the Prodigal Son, which we all use to be sometimes in the past until the Lord embraced us with his love and forgave us our sins. But until then, we could not sit down and wait as concerned parents; we knew we needed to do something and we needed a little extra help from the Lord. We could not stand the thought of losing our Son. How could any parent go to sleep, while their child kept bad company and become horribly influenced? How could any parent have their child derail on their watch and not do anything? How could a child who had all the good upbringing suddenly turn into a monster unknown to his parents? I knew I could not take it anymore and that something had to be done. It was not by my power though; in fact at that point I was completely nerve-wrecked and I had gotten to the end of myself. But by the power of the Most High God, I still carried on. I needed an answer, a solution and I was very determined to get one.

First, I went back to the Lord; the one who gave you to us out of His abundant mercy and wisdom. Guess what? One of the things He said to us was to look at ourselves in the mirror of His word. When we did, it was unbelievable who we saw and guess who? You of course. God must have a great sense of humour. You were our express image. The exact child we asked of the Lord. We saw you as a reflection of us. It felt as though a plug went out of my entire being. It was a revelation at that moment because ordinarily I could not see how that was possible. You became a constant reminder of who we are in Christ. You are a gift to us for our perfection, so that we can always see exactly who we are in Him. He then took us to the Scripture that says, *A son honours his father, and a servant his master. Then if I am a father, where is my honor? And if I am a master, where is my respect?'* He then challenged us to consider where His honour and His fear in our own lives were. All this time, He was waiting for his honour and His fear from us. He revealed to us how, in so many ways and in so many things, we had made wrong decisions and just like you, provoked Him to anger. Yet He reminded us that He is always patient, never giving up on us, never leaving us nor forsaking us. We realised then that we needed to live a life of victory for you to look up to. Yes we needed to leave a legacy of a victorious life in Christ Jesus.

He is still working in us to be like Him. The transformation is still ongoing, He has not finished yet; He is still moulding us into that which He wants us to be. Your dad knows something about art and he is always touching and retouching a work, which in my eyes should have been finished long ago. But to him, that work is far from being finished and I often wondered when it would be completed. Several times, he did tell me that a good piece of artwork is never finished; in fact it finishes only when the artist dies. I have also heard similar comments from builders – the builder says that a good house is the one that is not finished. We are like that in the hands of our creator. So Son, the Lord went ahead to tell us that our change of attitude would bring a transformation in your life, just as we are being transformed by His love in our daily lives. What a revelation! It gave me strength to love you unconditionally. It was not long after that revelation and our prompt response to it, that you came back. Just like the prodigal son's dad, we ran from a distance to embrace you, we forgave you and were determined to continue from where you stopped. We never stopped; we never gave up hope and prayer. We trusted that someday everything would be alright and we were right. You made your own decision to come back; this time no one compelled you to do so. I began to see changes in your life; I saw a huge transformation in your words, your actions, your choice of activities and friends. Truly the Lord preserved the seed of the righteous as He said he would.

You know that every revelation from the Lord is the truth, and the Bible says that we shall know the truth and the truth shall set us free. I knew the revelation was true because I recalled events that preceded your birth. At the time I prayed for a child, I wanted desperately to have a child like any other woman who got married and wanted to be a mother. I presented my selfish and superficial reasons to God but He never answered me as there were no reasons at all to make Him change His mind. I really had some stupid ideas Son; I wanted a child who would inherit our possessions when we are gone. You know everyone likes continuity. I had more reasons; I would like to get some mother's day cards and on such occasions be pampered like so many women who have children and get proper attention as a mother. Wait till you hear this; I even gave God some specifications. I told him I wanted a girl first and told my close friends how I would make her a perfect lady, teaching her how to talk, walk and dress. I was going to turn her into a little *diva*, shocking! I had a bag full of hair ribbons of different colours and stuff; the two things I did not buy in readiness for her arrival was a makeup kit and high heeled shoes. I reserved a name *'Olaedo'*, which means gold. We even went as far as building two special baby cots which we eventually gave away. *'Olaedo'* never came. It was later, much later after you were born that the Lord told me that *'Olaedo'* could not have had our image. Yes, I had planned to spoil her rotten, teach her the things I know from my head about how to be a lady, how to walk and talk like a lady thereby interrupting the plans of God.

Get me right, there is absolutely nothing wrong

with teaching your children all those, but you have to examine your motives when you do anything as a child of God. God knew that nothing good could have come out of it and that nothing will tamper with your originality and genuineness, which was why He sent you at the time He did. God loves us the way he made us although oftentimes we don't like the way we are and we want to alter things by ourselves. We alter our skin colour, the shape of our nose, the size of our breasts, buttocks or the way we speak. I can only try to change you. Remember God uses people who are themselves. But from the start, I was determined to recreate the baby girl to suit my desires. Consequently the Lord could not give her to us. He was not moved by my requests because He searched my heart and He saw what was in it. Silly requests don't make sense; as a result, no one answers them. You were full of requests when you were growing up, *'I want this, why can't I have that? My friends are all having this and that'*. If you could remember, the things or treats I gave you met genuine needs. In fact the more you made silly requests, the less you got the attention from me. God is exactly that way. Think about it, I may be wrong here but I believe it was indeed a strong request that we made to God and He granted it. God made us in His image; hence we have God's characters and features. He wants to see Himself and His reflection in us. He said *'go, be fruitful, multiply and subdue the earth'.* Multiplication as I understand it in this context is character duplication as against number multiplication. You multiply in grace, in honesty, in truth, in love, in kindness, in patience, in wisdom, in understanding, in power and in strength, because these are all parts of God's character. The only way we needed to know whether we were multiplying was through our seeds; seeds that will have our own image, and our reflections. You, Son, became *our mirror;* strange!

Since you came into our lives, life has been a journey; a journey full of different experiences and emotions. Sometimes we cry, at other times we laugh but most of the times we are joyful in the Lord, because He has commanded us to do so in every situation. The truth is that we overcame all that came our way, no matter what they were. God's grace has been more than sufficient for us and it's something to be thankful for. Not a single day did pass by without our gaining a new understanding and learning a new lesson. I have taken the time to tell you this story and to remind you of it once again, in case you have forgotten or doubted your identity. You did not just show up. Your arrival was orchestrated by God and you are His masterpiece. You were not an accident as the devil would want some people to believe about themselves. Remember Jeremiah? God told him that even before he was formed in his mother's womb, He knew him; He had previously counted the number of hairs on his head. So Son, God knew that special purpose for which He formed you and it is only just for His pleasure. Remember that everything that happens to you has been orchestrated by Him who knew you from the beginning to the end. Challenges do come your way as a child of God but note that they are for a purpose. The most important thing is to ask God to reveal the purpose of every challenge and to give you the wisdom and strength to go through it and to emerge successful on the other side. Therefore, we have lessons to learn from everything we go through and they become *wells of experiences* for us to draw from.

Son, this union you are about to go into is a journey of hope and faith. Some people call it an uncertain journey but I don't. My reason is that I know the person on the lead. He has already gone first. He has the map, the direction and the compass. He is the *GPS navigation system* and I am persuaded that He will lead you to his desired destination. He knows by heart where He wants you to be. Therefore, you have to ask God for strength to accept whatever He brings your way; that which is His perfect will. Don't ever be afraid to pray such prayers as *'thy will be done oh Lord'*, because you will soon find out that God has good plans for you; plans to do you good and not evil; to bring you to an expected end. If you do, you can be rest assured that He will lead you home. It will give me joy and pleasure to know that the two of you are living in peace and harmony, learning and understanding each other, complementing and completing each other and blending together to present one expression. Remember, people have their different idiosyncrasies, varying attributes or divine ministries. A good example is what you see in the Church. Not everyone is called to preach, not everyone is called to sing or be an usher, yet the Church has one single expression from people who have different ministries. Everyone is working according to their calling. A singer may not confidently teach but he is not to be envious of the teacher; he concentrates on the talent that God has given to him and tries to make the most out of it. He is still as relevant in the eyes of God as the teacher.

Back to our home, the fact that your dad cannot do the kind of things I do, like making sure the house is clean, cooking a very good meal, or even writing this letter does not make him less important or less productive than myself. He has his own areas of speciality, which I can't even venture into. If you think back, you will remember that I hate to mow the lawn. I know women who are experts at changing tyres on their cars, but I cannot remember turning a screw. Once, your dad went away for some days and the bulb in the dining room blew; we had to eat our dinner with candles until he returned. That was simply because I could not change the bulb. I never did anything like that; unbelievable! We did recognise our gifts and talents and we operated in our different God-given areas. Don't also forget that I am the one who does most of the talking, while he sits back and listens. Sometimes, I wonder if he would have married me, had he known that I could be such a chatterbox! Anyway, we are all used to that now. Remember how you saw us live at home. I'm not saying that you should model your relationship after ours. Sometimes I didn't even know what we were doing; however we still moved on by His grace and like the new wine, our relationship got sweeter and better by the day. I am only implying that you should follow good examples.

Speaking of role models, have you spoken to your uncles lately? You have to go and inform them as you are not living far away from them. Let them know what is going on in your life. They played strong roles in your life during your formative years. I remember when you used to go on holidays at their places. You always looked forward to visiting your cousins and sharing their toys. You were able to go to places that we never had time to bring you to. You used to tell us about how your uncle drove you and his kids (who were your mates) to the best parks you've ever visited. I still remember those days, when any new thing that happened to you was always the best thing that had happened to you. When you were brought to eat out, it was the best day of your life. When you were bought a new toy, it was the best thing that had ever happened to you. We got used to that a long time ago and I pray to God, Son, to give you that childlike mind in your marriage. May your union continue to be new every morning like God's steadfast love, so that it will always be the best thing that is happening in your life every moment. Let every one of your moments be new.

So, your uncle took you to the park and you came back from that holiday very excited about how good and aware your uncle was. So don't you ever forget that you owe him and your auntie that gratitude. Remember that if you love someone, you respect him; little wonder the Bible says *'owe no one anything but love'*. So, letting them know about such an important step you are about to take in your life shows love and respect. Can I entreat you, whatever you do, don't send them an e-mail or text, or even give that information to them through *Facebook.* I really do not assume that your uncle will appreciate it. Come to think of it, that's not how you were brought up. In fact, you weren't just brought up well; you were trained to respect yourself and to respect others. I witnessed a generation and I still see it, that has little regard or respect for other people or even for themselves. The society calls it *normative influence*. Is that the norm? Son, I refuse to be influenced in that manner or allow anyone to do that to you. When I saw you keeping friends who hung around in the dark to flirt with girls, I was ready to do anything to stop them potentially influencing you. If their actions were right, why did they wait until it was dark; why did they cover themselves and why would a child mess around with another child in the street? Those were children who did not understand the consequences of their actions. Would you have allowed that if they were your sisters? These were people's daughters. I could not stop them; did not try anyway, but I stopped you. I told you Son, that it could not happen under my watch, and reminded you that it would not be allowed as long as I housed you, fed you, clothed you and paid your fees. I reminded you that it was completely unacceptable under my roof. I made you to listen to radio programmes where concerned mothers like me bemoaned that same issue. Some celebrities also ran programmes on the topic. They called it '*if you respect me, respect my body*'. I was not completely a lone voice in the wilderness on this campaign. Bill Cosby used to be a household name on a television sitcom in those days when we had this conversation. I ran into one of his programmes, which was called *parenting programme for boys in the inner city.* In one of those programmes he said, *if you cannot live up to the consequence of your behaviour, it means that you are not responsible.* He went on to say that if you feel that you are responsible enough, wait until you get into the '*University of Massachusetts*'. If that university is too far away, wait till you get into any college at all. Your mum said any university at all, where you can be free, where you can have autonomy and where no one will scrutinise you from day to day. In fact that is any child's first step to independence – the university. They called your mum '*old school'*. I was not that as I had courage and confidence in my convictions. Unfortunately some of the boys' parents saw me that way and their excuse, Son, was that these guys could do worse things if not permitted to do this little. You may not have liked my point on that and I didn't expect you to; however, some mothers could not be bothered.

I allowed you do sleepovers a few times with your friends. On one of those occasions, your friend's mum let you guys out for too long wandering in the street, until a friend of mine who was coming back from a late-night shift saw you and decided to give me a call. I went to talk to your friend's mum in whose care I left you and her response was that you were with other kids and that there was no need to panic over kids staying out late at night roaming the streets. I never heard such a thing in my life; it was worse than my imagination could have drummed up. Although I am not against sleepovers but what a regret that experience was to me. How will anyone know that a small flame will not produce a huge fire? How could a mother who is supposed to be a carer, care less and how could I let you spend another minute in this woman's care. This goes to show how they care for their own children and how they define their own values. Therefore, respect and honour are good qualities a child of God should covet. In this relationship, you must honour and respect God and your bride, if you want to be respected. Note this Son, until then, she is God's, her body is God's, everything about her is God's and therefore God's property should not be touched or taken without His express permission; otherwise you will be looking for trouble.

Recently, we went around the shops looking for a gift, I saw a lot of fine things but didn't buy any. Not that I did not have money, no; nothing jumped out to me. I just needed to get a perfect gift, something that will give you joy, something for you to treasure. As you may know by now, I don't believe in asking people what they want as presents. My parents got me a perfect wedding present and up until now, you guys know how I love and cherish it. They knew me and knew what would suit me and they went for it. I would be silly not to tow that line. God did the same for us. He sent his only Son to save us. He did not ask us what we wanted, as He saw the need and in His wisdom, He gave us Jesus. He was perfect. No wonder the Bible says that *'every good and perfect gift comes from the Lord'* and that *'the gift of God makes rich and adds no sorrow'*. Think about it, if I ask you to choose, you may not choose right and you may end up sending it to the charity shop as an unwanted gift. Don't ask me how I know. I still remember those days at the toy shops. We used to spend hours unending, looking for a toy or present for you. When we eventually found one, you would be thrilled. But this happiness was only for a little while, until we got home, then you would discover that you really did not like it. The next thing I would hear was 'mum, I think I have changed my mind'. You always changed your little mind those days over the slightest thing; colour could make you change your mind at some point, it had to be blue or nothing. You have improved now I hope so. I know you may still have those tendencies, so I am not taking chances; I will take my time and just like God, I am going to buy you a wise gift. For now, I will pray about it a little while the more.

Can I suggest that you make two different cards, an invitation card and a thank you card? My reason is that people who attend your wedding will likely bring you gifts. Even if they don't bring anything, the gift of time is still a precious one. Remember, 'Time' they say, is precious. People who love God give Him the gift of their precious time. Anyway, back to my point. I think printing the thank you card is a good idea to show gratitude to your guests, you must also wait to get home before you open the gifts and don't try to *sneak a peek at the gifts.* I am sure you recognise that voice now. The voice of your mum telling you to wait till your birthday party is over before you start opening your gifts. You might mix them up in excitement and then you won't be able to recognise who gave you what and acknowledge them appropriately. I still do not know why I keep referring to your childhood and this gift thing; anyway just bring them all back home. I pray that you will both be pleasantly surprised and see them as blessings from family and friends, open them one by one and show gratitude to God and then to those who gave them to you.

Gratitude is one thing you must show in your life as long as you live; gratitude to God and to man. You must wake up to say *'thank you'* for every single thing, no matter how big or small. It was one of the difficult lessons you struggled with. I often had to remind you to say *thank you* to someone who had done you one favour or another and wondered, *'does he not like it, or was it not enough for him?'* I remember one summer, your dad and I put all our little resources together to send you and your brother to a weekend camp. We expected to have happy children when we came to collect you but that was not the case. After three days and two nights, you wanted more. You wanted us to pay more money so that you could join some other children on another trip without even returning home. What gave you that thought? Son, we were deeply disappointed. That attitude grieved us so much that we regretted sending you to the camp in the first place. You were always looking for more and sometimes not happy with what you had. Always remember that *'Godliness with contentment'*, the Bible says, *'is great gain'*. Recently you asked me why men marry more than one wife as was the case of my grandma; and why men go after other women. There are scores of reasons. Some men are lacking in commitment, others are not satisfied with what they have and are just curious about what the ones outside taste and feel like. *'Curiosity kills the cat,'* they say. By the time they realise it, they discover that she is the same if not worse than what they had at home. Anyway, you are wiser than this and you must always be aware of what you do. God does not like ungrateful people. In the Bible, out of the ten lepers that Jesus healed, only one of them came back to say *'thank you'*. Then Jesus asked, *'where are the other nine, what happened to them?'* Jesus recognised the only one that came to say thank you. He also hates people who are proud and people who tell lies. A '*lying tongue*' is how these people are referred to in the Bible. God also hates hearts that do not forgive, that is why He said that we should not let our anger last an extra day. These things are as simple as the little foxes that spoil the vineyard of love.

It has been a very eventful week and I was to tell you about the funeral we attended the other day, but I kept forgetting it. Could it be that I am still mindful of how you felt the first time you saw undertakers taking a coffin to a cemetery? You asked several questions as usual; 'why did they have long black cars, why were they all wearing black and long hats, why this and why that? Then you were not aware that death was final. Although I tried to explain everything, you kept wondering what would become of the man in the coffin. Would he be able to breathe when everyone had gone home; who is going to stay with him until he is ready to wake up?' I tried to explain to you again that he was not getting up in the physical and sadly he was going to be there with all his unused potentials, un-lived dreams and un-attained goals. Little wonder Dr. Myles Monroe said that the cemetery is the richest place to find wealth on earth; not the oil wells nor the gold nor the diamond mines; not even with the richest men and women in the Forbes list. His reason was that people die most times with all the good things God had deposited in them, without even realizing that they had them, let alone discovering or using them. Researchers according to him have found that only ten percent of the human brain is ever used. Shocking! Can you imagine what the world would look like if the people of this world maximized fully their God given potentials?

Conversely, I knew it did not mean much to you, because that was the stage of your life then. After that explanation, you turned around to dad and asked him, 'dad, are you going to die someday?' 'Yes' answered your dad, 'someday; someday when I am old enough to have completed my mission here on earth and have seen my grandchildren'. You asked him, 'dad, who is going to kill you?' Then you added, 'then all of us will take you to Disneyland and bury you there and you will continue to have fun even if you don't wake up'. That was really comical! Death can really be a mystery at every stage in one's life, but only the knowledge of God and faith in Christ Jesus can demystify it.

Yes, Mr. Smith is dead and has been buried. I'm sure you do remember him; the man you and your brother used to call Mr. Braggadocios. You boys were silly sometimes, giving people names other than what they were known by. Those innocent and unsuspecting teachers in your school had special names that you gave to them. I was shocked the day I discovered that you had names for your dad and I and we never knew. It was not funny and I frowned at it. But I got used to it and was comforted by the fact that the children of Israel also gave God different names at different times, depending on what He did for them at the time or their perceptions of Him.

We still use those names today to adore Him;

El Shaddai (Lord God Almighty),

El Elyon (The Most High God),

Adonai (Lord, Master),

Yahweh (Lord, Jehovah),

Jehovah Nissi (The Lord My Banner),

Jehovah-Raah (The Lord My Shepherd),

Jehovah Rapha (The Lord That Heals),

Jehovah Shammah (The Lord Is There),

Jehovah Tsidkenu
(The Lord Our Righteousness),

Jehovah Mekoddishkem
(The Lord Who Sanctifies You),

El Olam (The Everlasting God),

Elohim Qanna (The Jealous God),

Jehovah Jireh (The Lord Will Provide),

Jehovah Shalom (The Lord Is Peace),

Jehovah Sabaoth (The Lord of Hosts)

To Moses He said; call me *'I AM'*. That was a blank cheque; in other words, *'fill in the space with anything you need me to be for you and I will be that'*. John, in the book of Revelation, when he was on the Island of Patmos summed the name of the Lord up by calling him *'the beginning and the end'*. That was John. Son, for me He is Abba

Father. So, it is not bad when you give people names that you can identify them with. But make sure they are not derogatory, rude or funny as that becomes name-calling. Just make sure you are politically correct; these days you never can tell who is waiting for you at the door of the courts just for calling a name. So Mr. Smith died as a result of what he suffered in the hands of kidnappers some years back. He had achieved financial success in whatever he did and discovered that he could be a mini-god and thought that there was none as big as him. He used to be friends with us but when the money came, we no longer saw him. He took several mistresses and hosted parties unending. His poor wife and children suffered as a result of that lifestyle as he listened to no one and paid no attention to anyone's advice. He flaunted his money as though he was flying a kite. That was when you guys came up with that name *Braggadocios*. Unfortunately, his flamboyant lifestyle attracted the wrong people and did not last as long as he expected. He was kidnapped for a long time and after a ransom was paid for him to be released by concerned friends and relatives, he came home. When he came back, he was a different person. He was never the same Mr. Smith anymore and was very sick for a long time. His wife could not forgive him and every time we spoke to her about the need to forgive and to let go of the past, she would start from the beginning to recount every ill treatment she had ever received from her husband. We understood her. I remember vividly one early Saturday morning while we were still in bed, our doorbell was ringing non-stop and the Smith girls were banging at the same time. Your dad and I were very frightened and we nearly called the police. On a second thought, we decided to peep through the window first. When we eventually did, behold it was Mrs Smith and her two daughters; she was half naked. Apparently he did not allow her to leave with any of her stuff; he did not even allow her dress up properly. As she had no phone to make a call, her only option was to run into our house that morning. So she ran into our home with bruises on her head and blood stains all over her. Mr Smith had some drink the previous night as usual, and came home in the morning to batter her and her daughters. Vain and evil words were used, there was bitterness, hatred, resentment and she was not ready to forgive him. He died without making peace with his wife and children.

Son, you know your mum hates to tell stories about other people, but if I do tell you a person's story, just know that there is always a lesson to be learnt from it. You see, God wants us to be wealthy, He also promised to give us all that pertains to good life and Godliness. The book of Proverbs records that *'unending honour, wealth, riches and justice are his to distribute'*. However, when wealth, riches and honour come, we cannot afford to show off God's wealth and blessing as though we made it happen by our own strength. Remember the children of Israel; before they left Egypt, God did them a great favour by making them ask for gold and silver from their Egyptian neighbours. When they came to Mount Sinai, they used God's favour against God; they made a mini god with the silver and the gold. Some people today blessed with brain, beauty or children use them against God. For some, the moment they became wealthy will remember the land disputes their father had with the community and see it as the time to settle old scores. We cannot behave like people who have no wisdom. Instead, we should only boast in the Lord, knowing that all of these blessings come from Him and without Him we are nothing and we can do nothing. Now the Lord has blessed you from all sides; He has favoured you greatly and given you wealth and riches. Will you humble yourself before Him, in order to be honoured by Him? Remember, before honour is humility. Will you acknowledge that you have done nothing more than others to deserve His favour? God purposely drops a handful of wheat and barley for us to pick up, simply because we have found favour with Him. It is He who gives us power to create wealth and in His mercies He works behind the scenes on our behalf; it is not of our making, lest anyone should boast.

Ezigbo nwam (My beloved Son) I have a feeling that I will soon come to the end of this letter as I am beginning to sound like a dripping tap. It does not really depend on the volume of words, but the quality and what you make out of it. It's been seven days now since the thought of you pre-occupied my mind. Seven fun-packed days of reminiscing on the past, remembering all that we shared and thanking God for all that you meant to me. Seven days of trying to put all those thoughts together has shown me that words alone cannot truly describe my feelings for you and what all these mean to me. Without a doubt, you're sure beginning to understand my heartbeat better and the true purpose of this letter. It has taken me these seven days to spill out the deepest part of my heart to you. I have not really looked up from my writing because I have been trying to put down as much as I could remember, knowing that I have quite a good bit to write. At this moment, I feel like a fighter jet that took off a couple of days ago and is about to land, having accomplished its mission and I will get a proper rest from all my hard work. Now I can relax and enjoy the weather, which for some days now has improved a lot and I pray it stays so. Next on my priority is to get a proper rest, probably a massage from your dad will do. He knows that I have been writing this letter for days now and he completely approves of it. He is always working in the garden lately, just to make good use of the calm and pleasant weather. I took a few minutes out from my writing to see him, and guess what? I don't want your imagination running wild. Mrs. Collins, our opposite neighbour in the estate is renovating her house. Could that explain why you saw her at the home and furniture shop a few weeks ago? I never knew they had such a big garden. I did not go into their house anyway but I saw everything through their doors and windows, because all the curtains were stripped. Their house seems to be bigger than ours by just a few inches. Anyway, they are good people and I just hope that I will get an opportunity to go and see what they are doing. They seem to be very busy at whatever it is. That will also give us ideas for renovating our own house in the future. That is, if we are still going to be living here, which I doubt. In any case, your dad, I would imagine, has his own plans dusted by now.

Some things can act as a cover and you need to

uncover them before you see how they look on the inside. If Mrs Collins' house was not going through this renovation process and if those curtains were still hanging on her doors and windows, I wouldn't have been able to see through her entire house. This is like a marriage. Grandma use to say that marriage is like a wrapped gift. Whatever you see when you open it, is what you get. For now, you are still looking through the veil, till the day of your wedding, during which you will get the opportunity to remove the veil from the face of your beautiful bride. Then will both of you see each other clearly. You are going to see her for who she really is as there will no longer be a covering on her face. Above all, you will have total access to your bride, just like we have total access to Gods' throne of Grace because of the broken veil in the tabernacle that previously inhibited us from getting into the place where our God is. There will be no more hidden things; you will have no limitations; rather you will have boldness, no accusation from anyone, no conscience that pricks, or having to ask *should I or should I not*. I am also not going to be recounting Bill Cosby's rules of responsibility to you because you have fully come of age. You can imagine not having the boldness to talk to God directly in this present world. What could we have done? Where could we have been? Could it have been like having a bride as beautiful as yours, but then covered in a thick blanket of distance and legislations? Thank God the veil is finally broken and we are completely free to approach Him with boldness. Who would have believed that Mrs. Collins would let *passers-by* look into her house, considering how protective she was of her little haven? Mysteries!

Son, this new knowledge and awareness of a relationship does not just happen once. Rather it is the beginning of more revelations. You cannot say that you have known her after a few weeks, months or even years. It will be a continuous process as you both will soon discover. For her, it may be that you snore a lot or that you break wind under the duvet at night. Unfortunately you cannot deny it anymore as was the practice in the past when all I heard after that disgusting smell was *'not me; not me'*. You must realise that your breath can actually smell sometimes. If you forget to brush your teeth or use your mouthwash, or burp a few times in a row and forget that phrase *'excuse me'*, she will not be pleased. As if that's not enough, you can squeeze the toothpaste from the middle, and leave dirty clothes scattered all over the place. In fact, you can be really messy and can fight over nothing sometimes. Who knows what you would find out yourself? Hmm! Nothing strange Son, nothing strange. Paul in the Bible had an encounter with God and after the Lord revealed Himself to him, and performed all kinds of miracles through him, he still felt that he did not know God enough, and he prayed, *'that I may know Him, the power that raised Him from the dead, and the fellowship of His sufferings'*.

Shopping is one of the things you disliked as a

child or do I need to know you better in that area now? Have you done some personal shopping for yourself yet? Men hate shopping. Until now, your dad would always frown whenever I involve him in any form of shopping other than going to the hardware shops. If I managed to drag him, he stays a little while in the shop, and then before you knew what was happening, he had gone back to the car. I did not realise that when you guys were growing up, you were his excuse for not wanting to come with me, as he always told me that he wanted to look after you at home. Then when you were gone, he did not have any choice but to come with me. I am not implying that he does not shop. No, far from it, it's simply not his thing. However, he does have special shops he goes to, the ones that sell tools. He knows exactly what he wants, so it is only a matter of running in and out of the shop. He normally does that when he wants to fix any broken item in the house or when he remembers to build a new thing. Your dad fixes nearly anything. I do not have the slightest idea how he does it. All I needed to do was to point out that something was not working well and then sit back and watch him fix it, no matter how long it took him. He used to fix his car as well as your toys, which were always getting attention from his handyman skills. To this day, he fixes my jewellery, the toilets, the squeaky doors (mostly because he hates the noise they make) and he hangs pictures on the wall so perfectly and effortlessly like he was born to do that. I must confess it is a blessing to have him as my husband and I am totally impressed.

Growing up, you and your brothers were a bit like him; not so much at fixing broken things, but in not being willing to come to the shops with me, especially if it was a ladies clothes shop. I always bribed you by buying you sweets or something to hold, and when I didn't, you made the shopping experience a miserable one. Not a joke Son, the moment you saw my car or trolley move towards the direction of any fashion or cosmetic shop, you would start screaming *'Not again mum, oh no! Not again'*. You would surely make a scene and I would end up frustrated and head home instead. So the next time, your dad would offer to keep you, but I was unaware that it was not a favour he did for me, he just did not like shopping there as well. The least favourite gift or present anyone could give you was any form of clothing. You hated new clothes growing up and you would always ask me 'mum, why did you not buy us toys instead?' You would end up telling me that I had wasted all the money on clothes. I did not know why initially but I later realised that you did not like tidying your room. You hated folding things or putting them on hangers. The moment you saw me with new clothes, the next thing you said was 'mum, please get us new closet as well.' You were so funny. I remember one Christmas, we had put up the tree and got all the presents wrapped and placed under it. Just a day before Christmas, we went to pick up Auntie Nma from the airport. You were thrilled to see her and immediately started asking her what she got you for Christmas. You told her about the toys your friends had, and the latest ones for the season. She had quietly wrapped her presents, when you had gone to bed and placed them under the tree with others. On Christmas morning, as everyone opened their presents, we saw that your Auntie had bought you lots of clothes as Christmas presents. She had seen our needs from her last visit during which she noticed that things like children's clothing were so expensive here and she had told me on the phone not to go buying clothes for you. On that morning, as soon as you opened your present, your face told it all; you turned around and whispered to my ear,

'Mum'

'Yes', I said.

'Seriously?

Does she think that this is Halloween, when people dress up or something?' Mum, this is Christmas!

Fortunately, none of the clothes she got for you

looked anything like a Halloween costume; if anything, they were all expensive designer clothes for kids your age, which I could not buy for you at that time. But you just did not see the reason why she should buy you clothes as Christmas presents. Your Auntie and I tried very hard to understand what was worrying you. Growing up, we only expected Christmas clothes and were happy to get good meals afterwards. Your Christmas day was ruined as you would normally say, because you wanted toys and games. You refused to eat your Christmas dinner until your dad talked some sense into you.

Truly, I smile within myself when I look at you these days; you look very prim and proper, always well dressed in your expensive and executive suits. In fact, it feels like I have never seen you wear a jacket more than once. For sure, some day you are going to open up a shop for your used suits, shoes and ties, because at the rate you buy them, you will really need to do something about the clutter in your house very soon. Remember, you must tidy your clothes as soon as you take them off. I still want to know why you changed so much from not liking clothes to liking and buying even expensive ones. Is it all part of the growing up process or is it a generational thing? Oh well, I might as well go for the later, because your dad has grown up as much as he could and I still see not much changes in him. So back to the shopping, have you done them yet? What are you wearing on the wedding day? Is it a tuxedo or an ordinary suit? Are you wearing the same thing as your best man, and is every arrangement underway? Remember you don't have that much time to waste, so do not procrastinate. Just do as much as you can and make sure that you are always marking them off your list.

I am just giggling now, because my mind went back to what happened on our wedding day. Your dad and his best man wanted tailor-made suits and they went for it. For several weeks before the wedding, he called the tailor to remind him and the man promised him time and time again, that it was going to be ready in a few days time. The wedding day came and went and those suits never made it to our house. That was one of the biggest disappointments your dad had in his adult life. Son, on the eve of the wedding, your dad spent his whole time calling this man and he kept apologising and kept telling him that he was doing some finishing touches. The finishing touches continued until the morning of the wedding. As to what happened, your guess is as good as mine. He had to marry me in one of his old suits. He and his best man wore different colours, but thankfully, he was so still very good looking and I did not even notice it until after the wedding ceremony when he told me what happened. I could imagine that other people in the hall did not notice either; they all had their eyes on me. You can imagine how many people that man may have disappointed in the history of his business. He was a lazy man, who made light the gift that God gave to him, lacking in the spirit of excellence and I can predict that he is out of business by now. Never have anything to do with men without vision, because they and businesses do not go far together.

Can you do me a favour Son; no matter what it would cost you to dress your bride, my daughter in-law on the day of your wedding, just do it. Cover her up with the most expensive wedding gown you can afford. Remember, she is nothing but a princess, a daughter of the most-high God and you know she deserves the best. I know that she is in good financial shape and I have no doubt that she can afford any gown by herself. That was before she met you and I pray she will let you. Before we met Christ, we thought we could provide for ourselves and do so many things on our own, including covering our nakedness, but not anymore as we are now His bride. Christ is urging us to allow Him to cover us with his righteousness, to husband us, to take care of us, to carry our burdens. Please take good care of her, provide for her from the day you say *'I do'*. Love provides. God did not just love the world, He gave us....; He provided. You should be the leader, so lead by example and never for one minute think of transferring your provider role to her or another. Remember what the Bible says about a man who cannot provide for his household. It says that he is *'worse than an infidel'*. She is your full responsibility now.

'Is the Bible calling my friend Tony an infidel then, mum?'

Not at all Son, Tony lost his job a while ago because his company went bankrupt. It was not Tony's idea to let his wife provide for the family; it was situational and he is making every effort to get back to work. Every woman is best described as weak when they are around a man. In the Bible Ruth came to find strength in the bosom of Boaz and he provided and covered her. Please, cover her with your strength; clothe her for this occasion and always. Let your love continue to transform her into who God wants her to be, and I suppose you will love who God loves. In loving her, you will earn all her respect; not begrudging respect as is the norm with some women today. You will also receive the honour you deserve as her husband, but always remember that honour comes at a cost. Do not put too much consideration on the amount of money or resources it will take to buy her wedding gown, as long as she is very considerate and prudent in her spending. I believe she is. I am very sure you have plans for all these before now, because she really needs to appear as beautiful as a princess, considering that all eyes will be on her on that day. Her beauty will be a reflection of your goodness; kindness and generosity.

Things have changed a lot now compared to when I got married to your dad. Though the wedding was not particularly flamboyant, he was able to buy some beautiful things for me with his shoestring budget. My wedding ring still looks as beautiful as the day I first wore it and people always acknowledge that.

'How do you know that mum, you may ask. I know because whenever I am in a ladies gathering, someone usually notices and asks me about it. I am not bragging, get me right; your dad did not have to break the bank to get it, but it is beautiful, very stunning and exactly what I had envisaged. To say that I am completely impressed with my wedding ring is an understatement, and it gives me a great sense of pride, a sense of being loved. I have a feeling that it gives your dad a sense of pride as he has not stopped talking about how I was absolutely astounded the first time I saw the ring. Above all, the ring by my interpretation signifies an equal partnership forever; partners of one union with different roles. I have his authority and permission to represent him in most matters in his absence and as we grew older, we see things through each other's eyes. I can tell what your dad would approve of if he is not present and I can confidently take his place whether he is there or not. I can represent him at events, speak his mind, and make his choices as though he was there. Just the other day, as he was leaving for a business trip, he sent me to his friend, Mr Goodman, who deals on different selection of carriages for occasions, to look around to see what he has in case you allow us to hire one for your wedding. When it comes to such things, he trusts my judgement a lot, although he sometimes believes that I can be unfashionably honest. Mr Goodman has been his childhood friend, and they understand each other very well. You see, your dad has offered to hire a limo for you for this occasion, just to take that burden off your shoulders. That's what families do for their loved ones at such times. I also understand that your mother-in-law to be, who is a florist, has offered to provide all the flowers for decoration on that day. Please do not say no. I know you Son, no one is going to say that you are dependent on them. I would advise you to pocket your ego or sympathy and accept the love that family and friends will show you on this occasion. However you are not

compelled to accept them. Therefore if you two have any objections, don't hesitate to let us know. Your dad's friend is such an incredible fellow and is more than willing to let you have whatever car you prefer. When you need it, feel free to go to him, or even send him a note. I still remember how busy and stressful this period can be and he has been informed that you have this need.
Don't also forget to send him an invitation if you don't mind, because he's been a great friend of the family.

I am still not decided on what to wear on this special day, a day my beloved Son is going to have another rite of passage. A day that I have dreamt about all my life. A few seconds ago, my eyes went straight to my wedding picture with families from both sides. Looking at the photo, I took proper notice for the first time of what everyone wore. So much effort was put in by the women more than the men, especially the mothers of the bride and groom. Looking at my mum in this photo, she was very well dressed with her face beaming with satisfaction and your dad's mum was not looking bad either. It's obvious they spent time and thought on what to wear for weeks. The traditional attire both of them wore were well coordinated, especially in their colours. The men couldn't care less from what I could see from this photograph. They were grinning widely for the photographer. It was the usual suit, not really a surprise and very typical of men. I can also see my Grandma's happy face, with half her teeth disappeared from their usual positions, the strap of her bra loosely hanging from the sleeve of her traditional blouse like the straps of a handbag. These are sweet memories to cherish forever. A picture, they say paints a thousand words. That reminds me, have you thought of a photographer? I am sure both of you have good photographers to contact. These days, we have very good ones everywhere that you don't have to look far away to find one. However, by my understanding you must book in advance if you want their services;

just to be sure you have them booked in for the day. I honestly wonder how the photographers make money these days when people have smart-phones with cameras and video. I have discovered that on every occasion, people bring out their camera-phones to capture the moment. In fact, some friends will volunteer to take pictures of you with their cameras. But I think it is very important that you have a professional photographer to cover your wedding to avoid disappointments. A wedding is not something you can have another day. Apart from avoiding disappointment, a standby photographer really adds some fun to the occasion. Photographers, like many other professions keep evolving through the years, thanks to new technology. It used to be unbelievably hilarious during my mum's time. According to her, the photograph took about half the day as photo taking was a different ceremony on its own. The photographer used to be a man that had a long tripod stand covered with a red and black cloth. Every now and then he ran towards the people to either adjust their neck or their entire bodies. People smiled forever; often removing half of their make-ups. He would do this run over ten times, falling to the ground and getting up. When he felt that the people were not cooperating enough, he resorted to shouting and pointing at them with his fingers, all in a bid to reduce his runs. According to my mum, the long period of pointing and shouting, sometimes annoyed the people. Isn't it amazing how technology has improved things? These days someone can take a dozen photos of you in minutes without you knowing. Don't worry Son, everything will be alright. I will know when they will take the photos and I am not going to disappoint you this time. You had always complained of my smiling too much or not smiling at all in all the pictures that I took with you. You nearly cried over your graduation photograph, which was the only one that was taken by a professional photographer. It was too late to retake it as the gown had been returned. You won't believe that for this wedding,

I have been practicing on how to do a good pose and a good smile, because I need to get a good photograph that you will like, to make up for my past mistakes. I am nearly certain that whatever I decide to wear will be acceptable by you, hopefully. You are a grown man now and as such, I do not expect to see you look as embarrassed as you would normally do in those days. Back then, I can still remember those looks whenever I dressed up to come to your school or have a walk with you. Thankfully, that walk is no longer for me as I will only be in the corner, watching with joy and excitement. You are going to be walking with the love of your life, your better half and your beautiful bride. Remember to follow the rules by arriving on time at the altar before her and standing where you will be asked to stand by the officiating minister. Of course, that morning is not the time to look for your car keys and wallet as you normally did, for you will not be carrying any. Your best man would be in possession of those, including the embarrassing speech you wish he does not make. I am quite sure you will be looking dapper and even better in that grey suit paired with a white bow tie, or have you changed your mind on the colours? Anyway, make sure you wait patiently until she joins you. We will all wait with you as the bride walks down the aisle, probably with her father by her side. I am looking forward to hearing that song *'here comes the bride'* accompanied by harps and violins playing in the background, like you two always wanted. We will all wait as she glides down the aisle looking stunning in her beautiful gown. Wait as you had always waited; don't be in a hurry and please let her take her time to get there as in all things. Wait in hope; wait in love and in faith. Soon you will discover that marriage is a journey of faith and patience. Therefore you must wait patiently for her in all things and at all times. Never rush her or be in a hurry. Be rest assured that we will all be there with you and for you as you take the first step in this journey. We will cheer and shout with joy as soon as we see her join you at the altar. We will listen with the host of heaven as you read your vows to her, which sometimes could go like this:

I, Adam, take you, Ada,
To be my lawful wedded wife,
To have and to hold,
For better or for worse,
For richer, for poorer,
In sickness and in health,
To love and to cherish;
From this day forward
Till death do us part.

Remember, it's a covenant and a commitment to love her all the days of your life, a covenant to say that you will never hurt her under any situation or circumstance. This covenant says that you are going to accept her for who she is and for whom she will become. Above all, it places her as the number one priority in your life. We will all clap and cheer for joy the moment your lips meet each other. The kiss that will forever signify a holy union, sealed for eternity. It must be a very special moment, the moment when you two will be introduced as man and wife, the moment when she takes on your name; the moment everyone, including your mum, will be honoured and God will be glorified. I don't hope to shed any more tears at that moment Son. I have released you with my whole heart to cleave to her. If I do, it won't be in pain, no, it will all be for joy and to the praise of Him who makes all things possible.

Ps

I have finally come up with an idea of a gift for you and you will find it in a brown envelope with the words: *Dearest Son*

It may not look big but remember, fine things they say, come in small packages. It may not look very fanciful but remember, content matters more than packaging. Inside this brown envelope is all that you will need for this whole journey. It will remind you of the word of God, which has eternal, immeasurable and innumerable values, the benefits of which you will forever treasure. Remember, heaven and earth will pass away, but the word of God will endure forever. It's a complete guide to where you are going. It is true and self-explanatory if you seek to know. It's a copy of this letter and on the envelope is written *'Dearest Son'*; A gift from the deepest part of my heart.

I hope you will value it.

Happy married life Son, may the Lord keep and preserve you both, may his countenance shine upon you both continually and may He give you peace, the peace that passes all understanding. Congratulations, Son.
I love you.
Mum.